THE
SPACE RACE

THE
SPACE RACE

From Sputnik to Shuttle:
the story of the battle for
the heavens

JON TRUX

NEW ENGLISH LIBRARY

Grateful thanks to the Novosti Picture Agency for permission to reproduce all the Russian photographs.

Grateful thanks to the NASA Picture Agency for permission to reproduce all the American photographs, which were supplied by the Science Photo Library, London.

Grateful thanks to Popperfoto for permission to reproduce the photograph of the V2 on page 10.

Picture Researchers:

Russian photographs – Maggie Murphy-Ferris and Jon Trux

American photographs – Carl Esch and Jon Trux

First published in Great Britain by New English Library, Mill Road, Dunton Green, Sevenoaks, Kent, a division of Hodder & Stoughton Ltd, in 1985

Editorial Office: 47 Bedford Square, London, WC1B 3DP

Designed by Youé and Spooner Ltd, Croydon, Surrey.

Typeset by South Bucks Photosetters

Printed in Italy

ISBN: 0 450 06046 2

CONTENTS

1 THE BIRTH OF THE SPACE RACE

CHAPTER ONE
THE ROCKET CZARS   8

CHAPTER TWO
THE NEW FRONTIER   17

CHAPTER THREE
THE COLD WAR WARRIORS   36

CHAPTER FOUR
RIDING THE FIRE   49

2 THE GREAT COSMIC OLYMPIAD

CHAPTER FIVE
DEATH AND DISASTER   66

CHAPTER SIX
THE MOON AT CHRISTMAS   74

CHAPTER SEVEN
ONE SMALL STEP   84

CHAPTER EIGHT
THE LAST MEN ON THE MOON   100

3 COLONISTS ON THE EDGE OF SPACE

CHAPTER NINE
THE WAVE OF THE FUTURE   118

CHAPTER TEN
DACHAS IN THE SKY   135

CHAPTER ELEVEN
THE WIDE BLACK YONDER   146

INDEX   160

'We are all in the gutter, but some of us are looking at the stars.'

Oscar Wilde

'What do Sputniks give to a person like me? So much money is spent on Sputniks it makes people gasp. If there were no Sputniks the Government could cut the cost of cloth for an overcoat in half and put a few electric flat-irons in the stores. Rockets, rockets, rockets. Who needs them now?'

a Russian worker on Pravda

1 THE BIRTH OF THE SPACE RACE

THE DATE is 4 October, 1957, and the scene a windswept ridge, high above the icy steppes of central Russia. Stars hang like frozen diamonds in the clear night sky.

Thousands of labourers have converted a natural bay into a 200ft-deep pit, a full half-mile wide, over which juts a solid concrete shelf. On this shelf sits a squat, tapered rocket, reflecting the glare from banks of floodlights. Mist wreaths the flanks of the rocket.

The expanse of concrete and steel is empty and still. Its creators are back in their prison camps. The rocket engineers, who have assembled the giant missile; who have toiled against time to check and re-check the twenty engines; who have carefully placed a metal sphere inside the nose of the beast; who have edged the assembled launcher down railway tracks to the pit's edge; who have lifted it into the vertical position and pumped hundreds of tons of volatile liquid oxygen and kerosene into its tank are nervously manning consoles in a bunker a few hundred feet away.

Through periscopes, the crew can see the silhouette of the rocket as it sits clamped to the steel arms of the launch tower. Suddenly a searchlight picks out the figure of a young man next to the tower. With a flourish he raises a bugle to his lips, and a fanfare rings out across the bay. The searchlight pans across the rocket, the youth disappears, and the countdown resumes.

The atmosphere in the bunker is tense. Each time the countdown nears single figures, someone reports a bad connection or a faulty meter. They wait impatiently until the count is resumed.

Only one man seems unperturbed. He is the Chief Designer: Sergei Korolev, veteran rocket engineer, Gulag survivor, now Premier Nikita Khrushchev's protege. There he sits, microphone in hand, calmly directing the launch.

Finally, the count reaches zero. The launch tower folds down like the petals of a flower. Twenty engines thunder into life, sending streams of fire cascading across the bay. The steppes, bathed in light, send the echoes back to the watchers in the bunker.

Metre by metre the rocket edges upwards on a tail of fire, turning eastwards towards the dawn. They pull on overcoats, run from the bunker, watch excitedly as the four boosters burn out and drop away, leaving a white-hot spark climbing up into the clear night sky. Sputnik 1 is heading for space! Sergei Korolev has launched the world's first satellite! The assault on space has begun!

The visionary: Sergei Korolev directs Russia's assault on space.

CHAPTER ONE

THE ROCKET CZARS

IN THE spring of 1945, the Allied armies raced towards Berlin and the fall of the Third Reich. One of their targets was the German rocket establishment at Peenemunde, on the Baltic coast, where engineers under Wernher von Braun designed and flew the world's first ballistic missile — the V-2.

Von Braun had been building rockets since the age of 18, when he joined a group of similar enthusiasts who called themselves the Society For Space Travel. This group of dedicated amateurs constructed dozens of small, noisy and dangerous devices until complaints from the neighbours stopped them. Though the Society's interest was purely scientific, its work was soon co-opted by the German Army, who saw rockets as a way round the arms limitations placed on Germany by the Treaty of Versailles at the end of World War I.

By 1943, von Braun and the Peenemunde team had successfully launched a rocket with a one-ton warhead and a range of 200 miles: the V (for Vengeance)-2.

Although the Peenemunde group was working for Hitler, they were more interested in space travel than war rockets. ('Oh yes, we shall get to the moon,' said von Braun to a colleague, 'but of course I daren't tell Hitler.') Designs for a manned V-2, with a pressurised cockpit instead of a warhead, were kept well

Wernher von Braun, arm in plaster, surrenders with fellow Peenemunde engineers to (far left) US Counter Intelligence Officer, April 1945. Said one German scientist: 'We despised the French; we were afraid of the Russians; and we didn't think the British could afford us. That left the Americans.'

hidden from the prying eyes of the Gestapo. Several members of the group were interrogated and arrested — including von Braun.

Against the V-2 there was no defence. The rockets travelled too high and quickly for detection. Both the Allies and their erstwhile Russian partners were aware of the long shadow this new and terrifying invention would cast over the future of the post-war world.

It was the Russians who first entered Peenemunde, but it was a Pyrrhic victory: von Braun and the top-ranking engineers had fled westward to surrender to the Americans.

The Soviets were left with a mass of rubble: what remained of Peenemunde after British bombing had been systematically destroyed by the retreating Germans. Only the underground production plant for V-2s survived, and that fell into American hands.

The US moved fast, shipping the Peenemunde group and a hundred V-2s back to the safety of America via a top-secret organisation, Project Paperclip. Under an agreement with the Russians, all V-2 booty was to be shared, but the first trainload of hardware destined for the Soviet zone was hijacked by the US Army. Instead of rockets, the Russians got rusty farm machinery.

'This is intolerable!' thundered Joseph Stalin. 'We defeated the Nazi armies; we occupied Berlin and Peenemunde; but the Americans got the rocket engineers.'

In addition to the rank-and-file engineers left behind in the panic and the smoking remains of Peenemunde, Stalin's armies gleaned the all-important list of component suppliers. All was not lost: most of the component factories were now in the Russian zone. The Soviets, like the Americans, were now about to use the V-2 project for their own ends, and the man appointed by Stalin to head the new venture was Sergei Korolev.

Like Wernher von Braun, Korolev was obsessed with the possibility of space travel. He too was a man of great talent; a visionary as well as a scientist and engineer.

Though the two men never met, their lives were dramatically similar. The young Korolev, who had studied aeronautics under the master designer Tupolev, discovered a passion for the emerging science of rocketry and joined a small club of similar enthusiasts: GIRD, the Group Studying Rocket Propulsion.

This was during the 1930s, the great age of rocket experiments. All over Europe and the United States, amateur groups like GIRD and von Braun's VfR were deafening their neighbours with noisy and dangerous devices. The rocket clubs were ill-equipped and short of money, but they proved that the new devices worked.

Though the rocket clubs were only interested in the exploration of space, it was the military possibilities of the new engines which attracted patronage. In GIRD's case, this took the form of Soviet Arms Minister Tukachevsky. The rocket group was absorbed by the Red Army, and Korolev went with it.

Then came the Stalin purges, and Korolev entered the world of the vanished. The Soviet dictator accused Tukachevsky of plotting against him, and all those who worked under the Arms Minister were rounded up and sent to exile or death. Korolev survived the long journey to Siberia and a year's forced labour in the infamous Kolyma Gulag. There, like so many, he might have rotted.

The agent of his salvation was his former mentor, Tupolev, himself a victim of Stalin's paranoia. Since the veteran plane designer's expertise was vital to the State, he was incarcerated in an open prison, free to carry out military work. When Hitler invaded Russia, Tupolev was ordered to employ top engineers now resident in the Gulags. The secret police who had dispatched Korolev to Kolyma were sent to rescue him.

As the German Army advanced on Moscow in the fearsome winter of 1941, the Tupolev group was evacuated under armed guard to safety in the East. By yet another stroke of good fortune, Korolev fell in with a former GIRD colleague and ended the war working on military rocket research. He was still under a life sentence for treason.

While von Braun was *en route* for America, Sergei Korolev supervised the shipments of V-2 hardware back to the USSR. He also located the hundreds of German engineers living in the Soviet zone. These unfortunates were rounded up and taken to Russia, where they were systematically drained of their knowledge. Many never returned home until the 1950s.

Korolev, though an 'unperson', rose rapidly in the Soviet hierachy. Nevertheless he was only allowed to watch a demonstration V-2 launch in the British zone from beyond the perimeter fence. The British wouldn't let him inside without an I.D. card, which the Soviets wouldn't give him. Korolev was not to be trusted.

Yet two years later, Korolev was in charge of the Russian ballistic missile team, building Stalin's first war rocket: 'An effective straitjacket,' said Stalin, 'for that noisy shopkeeper Harry Truman.'

The dictator never lived to see his 'straitjacket' fly. He was succeeded by Nikita Khrushchev, a shrewd peasant politician and ranter, with a taste for publicity stunts which would show the world the supremacy of the Soviet socialist system under his personal leadership.

British test-fire captured V2 missile. Outside the wire, Sergei Korolev watches, then returns to Russia as 'Chief Designer'.

One of his first acts as Premier was the release of thousands of Gulag victims, not through philanthropy but through Khrushchev's desire for his own power base. Under Stalin, these men and women had lost all hope. The new Premier was offering them freedom in return for loyalty.

This was to be Korolev's fate. There was a price on his freedom: Khrushchev took the glory for everything Korolev achieved. While Korolev lived, he was referred to only as the mysterious 'Chief Designer' whose exploits so vexed the United States. Only after his death was his name and role revealed.

It was now the early days of the Cold War, and the dawn of the nuclear age. Though Khrushchev had the Atomic Bomb, it was a useless bargaining counter. The Soviet Union had no bombers capable of flying to the US and back.

Missiles were to be the answer to the American bomber fleets. Since Stalin had kept the very existence of his 'straitjacket' under wraps, Korolev was summoned to the Kremlin to tell his new masters all about it. As Khrushchev recalled in his memoirs:

> I don't want to exaggerate, but I'd say we gawked at what he showed us as if we were sheep seeing a new gate for the first time. When he showed us one of his rockets, we thought it looked like nothing but a huge cigar-shaped tube, and we didn't believe it would fly. Korolev took us on a tour of the launching pad and tried to explain to us how a rocket worked. We were like peasants in a marketplace. We walked round the rocket touching it, tapping it to see if it was sturdy enough — we did everything but lick it to see how it tasted. . . We had absolute confidence in Comrade Korolev. When he expounded his ideas, you could see passion burning in his eyes.

Korolev's passion was for space travel, not missiles, but if Khrushchev needed Korolev to build the rockets he would rattle at the West, then the Chief Designer needed the canny Premier to act as his paymaster.

Khrushchev's new toy, the H-Bomb, weighed nearly two tons. To throw

Khrushchev (centre) chats with Kazakhstan farmers. A shrewd politician with a penchant for the spectacular, Khrushchev soon realised the propaganda value of space stunts.

such a device into the United States, Korolev needed to build a rocket that would be three times as powerful as the nearest US equivalent (the Atlas, then still on the drawing board). This he achieved by clustering dozens of small but reliable rocket engines into a central core, surrounded by four identical tapered boosters. It was called by a variety of names: officially, the R-7; Korolev's team dubbed it 'semyorka', 'old number seven'; and US intelligence referred to it as 'The Beast'. By whichever name it was called, the rocket was a clumsy monster which required each of the twenty-odd engines to fire simultaneously, but it worked.

Though the first prototypes blew apart or trailed off crazily into the heavens, by early 1957 the Chief Designer had succeeded in firing an R-7 thousands of miles into the Pacific Ocean.

Khrushchev's celebrations were short-lived. Though he now possessed the world's first transcontinental rocket, fireworks of another sort were exploding in his ears. Palace intrigues within the Kremlin were undermining the Premier's hold on Russia, while his image abroad was shaken by the brutal suppression of the Hungarian uprising a year before. He needed a new propaganda coup, and he needed it fast. It was time to reconsider Korolev's proposal for an earth satellite.

Sputnik 1, first artificial earth satellite and Russia's challenge to the West. The space race has begun, and it's Russia 1, America 0.

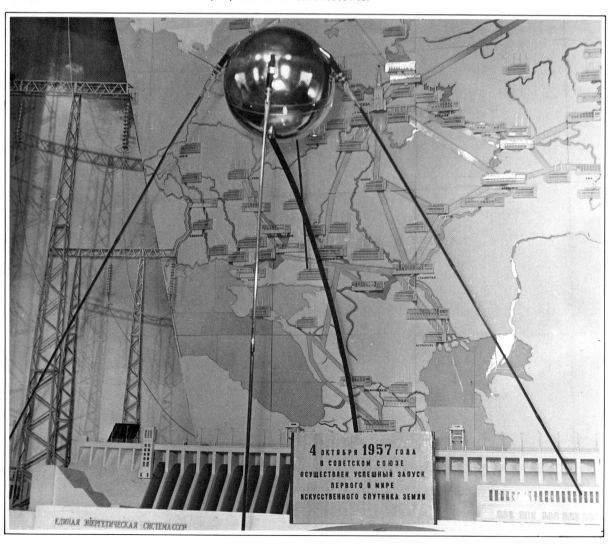

The Chief Designer had argued since 1954 that it was possible for the USSR to orbit a simple satellite, using a modified semyorka as a launcher. The calculations were there: the power of the R-7 could enable a small package to escape earth's gravity. A typical reaction to Korolev's lobbying was 'Not interested in fantasy: I visualise a space shot only in the year 2000.'

Despite the rebuffs, he persevered, designing a satellite (which he dubbed 'the simplest'), making modifications to the R-7, and producing the detailed calculations which would determine 'the simplest's' everlasting free-fall. Now it was Khrushchev's turn to listen. He gave Korolev the go-ahead, on condition that the satellite would be launched on 4 October: the fiftieth anniversary of the Russian Revolution. Khrushchev's deadline, compounded by the knowledge that the Americans were preparing for a space shot as part of an international scientific study, forced Korolev into a race against time. He lived on the project, in a small timber house halfway between the assembly hall — a box of a building where the R-7's stages were mated together — and the launchpad.

Here he put the finishing touches to his 'simplest', designing it as a blend of romance and propaganda. It was called Sputnik, which translated as 'fellow traveller', and the shape was simple and expressive: a sphere, the natural form of stars and planets. Instead of the scientific instruments Korolev would have preferred, the crippling schedule forced him to settle for a battery-powered radio. For maximum effect, he chose a popular short-wave frequency and an orbit that would bring Sputnik over Europe, Asia and the United States. Khrushchev wanted the whole world to know that Russia, not America, had launched the first earth satellite.

A few days before the target date, Korolev supervised the loading of the metal beach-ball with its four swept-back antennae. Swarms of technicians clambered over the R-7 as it lay in the assembly hall. The air was charged with tension as one of the crew flipped a console switch, activating Sputnik's transmitter. Then the vast room fell silent as the distinctive bleat of Sputnik 1 echoed across the hall.

'That,' said Korolev, 'is the sound of the future.'

Lyndon B. Johnson, then a Senator, was at his Texas ranch when he received word that the Soviet Union had successfully launched the world's first satellite. After supper, Johnson strolled out into the evening and saw the tiny point of light moving across the sky:

'That sky,' he mused, 'had always been so friendly, and had brought us beautiful stars and moonlight and comfort; all at once it seemed to have some question marks all over it. . . I guess for the first time I started to realise that this country of mine might perhaps not be ahead in everything.'

Johnson's reactions were shared by most of America. Not since Pearl Harbor had Americans felt so vulnerable. The country, said the **New York Times**, was in 'a race for survival'. Walter Cronkite commented on Sputnik's radio signature thus: 'Until two days ago that sound had never been heard on this earth. Suddenly, it has become as much a part of twentieth-century life as the whirr of your vacuum cleaner.'

While some Americans downplayed the achievement ('This satellite is a hunk of iron that anyone could launch,' scoffed one Admiral) the popular consensus was that the Communists had established a toe-hold in space and the United States had been humbled as a result.

Why, Americans asked themselves, had this happened?

The United States also made good use of its V-2 booty. Rocket after rocket roared into the clear blue desert sky above White Sands proving ground in New Mexico. Facilities were basic, safety precautions non-existent. The mood was 'get the engines lit and see what happens'. Workers often scattered for shelter as the missiles misfired and fell back on them. Even after a concrete blockhouse was provided, excited engineers would rush outside to watch the latest shot. This practice ended only after a V-2 nosed over, the crew ran back in, and the rocket executed a direct hit on the refuge.

Occasionally, civilians would witness the wrath of the engineers' new playthings. One V-2 made an unauthorised visit to Mexico, landing on a cemetery in Ciudad Juarez. An international incident was averted only because it was fiesta time, and the revellers roared with appreciation at the new firework.

It was the post-war era for America. The country basked in the sunshine of the new consumer society: televisions, man-made fibres, a convertible on every driveway. Apart from the shadow thrown by the Iron Curtain, the future looked good. No-one was in a hurry to be the first into space, least of all the President.

Eisenhower was in the White House, and he took little interest in the notion of space as a propaganda tool. Neither did he have much faith in the military-related establishment that Khrushchev used to so much effect. It was Ike, after all, who coined the phrase 'military-industrial complex'.

If the politicians couldn't see it, the military were too busy haggling over who should get von Braun and his German V-2 specialists. The Navy had proposed a satellite launch as early as 1945, but no-one paid much attention to it. There followed a spate of ideas from the Army and Air Force: so many, in fact, that the White House couldn't decide between them.

As far as the scientists and engineers were concerned, the 'sexy' projects were intercontinental missiles and the manned rocket planes that test pilots were throwing around the skies of California. Satellites and space travel were regarded as 'too Buck Rogers' to be taken seriously. Even the White Sands pioneers, who were breaking altitude records by the batch, kept a low profile.

The first Soviet H-Bomb test, in 1953, took America by surprise and shattered the nation's complacency. The Reds were thought to be years away from such a device. When US intelligence warned that Khrushchev's engineers were about to present him with an intercontinental missile, the country was panicked by a nightmare vision of giant H-Bomb-tipped Soviet rockets burning America from coast to coast.

The fact that Korolev's semyorka was only being produced in small numbers and was a completely ineffective ICBM eluded US intelligence, who asserted that R-7s were rolling off the production lines like cars in Detroit. When the Soviets announced, in the autumn of 1957, that they had tested a 'super long-distance rocket', the US was aghast. 'We captured the wrong Germans!' roared a four-star General, and journalists across the nation began writing of 'the missile gap'. Since the US was ahead in H-Bomb technology and was confidently talking of bombs no larger than oil drums, rocket engineers were building small, highly-sophisticated missiles: racing cars to Korolev's Model T.

Wernher von Braun, now working for the US Army, was one of the few people in America to understand that space was to be the new area of competition between Russia and the United States. As early as 1954, the German rocket pioneer proposed sending a simple satellite into space aboard an Army Redstone rocket, itself derived from his earlier V-2. 'Project Orbiter', as it was called, would have been fast and cheap, but it lost out to a purpose-built launcher, Vanguard.

This was to be the 'official' US contribution to the forthcoming International Geophysical Year, a programme of international studies in earth sciences. While Korolev raced against time to ready Sputnik, the Vanguard project just cruised along at its own speed.

After the bombshell news of Sputnik, Ike answered his critics with the assertion that the 'satellite program has never been conducted as a race with other nations'. It was a classic example of missing the point. As far as Khrushchev was concerned, there was a 'space race' just as there was a 'missile race'. Sputnik and its successors would show the world that Russia was an advanced society, competing with the West on equal terms. No longer would the Soviet Union be the underdog in world affairs. Of course, that glory would reflect well off Premier Khrushchev. . .

As Sputnik bleeped around the world, Wernher von Braun and his 'wrong Germans' were hosting a cocktail party at Huntsville, Alabama, home of the Army missile organisation. His guests were a group of politicians and Army top brass. After the shock had died down, they discussed reviving Project Orbiter, the quick-and-dirty satellite project. He was asked how long it would take for Project Orbiter to reach the launchpad. 'Ninety days' was the answer, but again the White House prevaricated.

Instead, a month after Sputnik 1, Korolev sent a second, larger Sputnik into orbit, and this time it carried a passenger: Laika, the world's first canine space traveller. 'The Red Pupnik!' screamed a US newspaper. In London, the Canine Defence League protested to the Russian Embassy, then called on dog-lovers

'Kaputnik!' America's answer to Sputnik falls back in flames . . . live on TV. 'One hundred million dollars has just gone up in smoke,' comments TV newsman.

everywhere to 'observe a silent minute at eleven o'clock each morning while this dog is in outer space.' Laika stayed alive for a week, proving that an animal could survive the rigours of spaceflight, then died (presumably painlessly) when her oxygen supply ran out.

Finally, on 16 December, 1957, the first US satellite, Vanguard 1, was ready for launch. Although the Vanguard group claimed they were planning only a dry run, the White House announced it as the long-overdue US satellite attempt — the morale booster that would restore American prestige.

Swarms of newsmen descended on Cape Canaveral, Florida, to cover the historic event. The TV cameras rolled, the countdown reached zero, and the slim pencil-shaped Vanguard lifted six inches off the pad. . . only to fall back in a ball of fire, the classic exploding cigar trick. As the rocket disintegrated, the fifty-pound satellite was thrown free and rolled across the wet sand, its tiny transmitter chirping merrily.

The catastrophe was total. 'Kaputnik!' was one news headline. The Russians had orbited a half-ton spaceship with a dog on board, and the Americans couldn't throw a tiny satellite higher than the launch tower, *and* the humiliation had been witnessed live on TV.

Five days later, the White House gave Wernher von Braun the go-ahead for Project Orbiter, and within ninety days, just as he'd promised, a modified Army Redstone missile lobbed the first US satellite into orbit around the earth. Explorer 1 weighed a mere 31lbs, but it discovered a zone of radiation girdling the earth and, which was of more importance to two hundred million Americans, it carried the Stars and Stripes into space.

Success at last. Von Braun (right) and colleagues celebrate America's first satellite, Explorer 1. Amid the euphoria, it was left to the rocket pioneer to warn: 'We are competing only in spirit . . . we have not seen the last of the Soviet space rockets.'

CHAPTER TWO

THE NEW FRONTIER

'I want to be firstest with the mostest in space, and
I just don't want to wait for years!'
— US politician James Fulton.

O N THE last day of July, 1958, more than eight thousand people left
work for the last time as employees of NACA, the National Advisory
Committee for Aeronautics. Next morning they returned to the same
jobs as employees of a new Federal organisation, the National Aeronautics
and Space Administration, NASA — an acronym as familiar today as the
Coca-Cola logo.

Eisenhower was under pressure to get the US ahead in space. One politician
suggested that the US should ready a rocket to fire blue dust at the moon, just
in case the Russians bombed the moon with red dye. 'Then,' he said without

Luckless chimp Ham prepares to ride an
ejection seat. Before humans took to the
heavens, animals were used as unwilling test
subjects. Ham goes on to greater glory as the
first 'American' into space.

batting an eyelid, 'the moon would be red, white and blue!'

The generals wanted a military space programme: 'Space,' boomed General Thomas D. White 'is the natural and logical extension of air; space power is merely the cumulative result of the evolutionary growth of air power!'

Ike was not convinced, The American thrust into space should be conducted openly, he argued, not behind a cloud of military secrecy. The obvious civilian candidate was NACA, which for nearly forty years had conducted research and testing in all areas of aviation. Even now, NACA was flying the X-series of rocket planes, the biggest, fastest and newest of which was the X-15, a black stub-winged monster with an engine more powerful than the ill-fated Vanguard. NACA had plans for the X-15, involving speeds up to 5000mph and a height of fifty miles, right up to the edge of space. Some people were even talking about strapping the X-15 to two big booster rockets and running it around the earth a couple of times.

So NACA became NASA, and within a year had acquired the Army missile organisation at Redstone Arsenal and the test range at Cape Canaveral — much to the generals' chagrin, since this included Wernher von Braun and 5000 engineers, and a hundred million dollars' worth of labs, test stands, launch pads and machine shops. The young Agency now had the talent and the hardware to wrestle with the Russians for control of the heavens.

If the Americans were to compete seriously, they needed to put a man into space. Such a project had already been talked about — MISS, or Man In Space Soonest, a quick-and-dirty plan to use an existing ICBM to launch a human passenger in a hundred-mile arc over the Atlantic Ocean. The X-15 plan had been considered and dismissed: the boosters were still on the drawing-board and there were severe problems with the heat of re-entry. It would take another decade for the concept of a winged rocket-glider to be revived.

The MISS idea was crude — one NASA official grumbled that 'it had about the same technical value as the circus stunt of shooting a young lady from a cannon' — but it had the advantage of simplicity and speed. On 7 October, 1958, MISS was announced to the world as Project Mercury: to 'send a man into orbit, investigate his capabilities and reactions in space and return him safely to earth'. The orbital attempt, using an Atlas ICBM, would be preceded by the original MISS 'human cannonball', using the less powerful but off-the-shelf Redstone. NASA just kept its collective fingers crossed and hoped that the Russians wouldn't do it first.

The big question was, could a man survive?

Looking at it objectively, the idea of hurling a man into the unknown reaches of outer space summoned up images of the worst kind of torture. Take g-forces (in fact, much of the early work on the effect of multiples of the force of gravity on the human frame were undertaken by the Luftwaffe in wartime concentration camps — the results, seen on film, are horrible). On launch and re-entry, astronauts would face up to twenty times normal gravity. Would they survive, or would they return with their vital organs mangled? What about meteoroids? Out in space, they might riddle a space capsule. Or cosmic radiation, which slams into the earth's atmosphere at the speed of light? How much could a human take? And what of the fundamental question: could a man survive outside the womb of his home planet, outside gravity's caress, or would he return a zombie, his synapses burnt out by the awful strangeness of space?

It was no wonder that sci-fi movies of the time showed returning astronauts stark raving mad, hideously mutated by radiation, or spattered over the cabin walls.

Hence the major task of early satellites was to test this strange world for radiation and meteoroids — neither of which, it turned out, showed serious dangers for a space voyager. Likewise, test pilots flew zero-g arcs in jet fighters and rocket planes and showed that brief periods of weightlessness were harmless and even enjoyable. In a formidable display of masochism in the name of science, Captain Eli L. Beeding rode a rocket-powered sled to prove that a human being could take an impact force of no fewer than 83 gs. During his split-second decelleration into a water-filled trough, Beeding weighed seven tons. His record has never been beaten.

The g-force effect was also explored on the centrifuge, a vicious version of the fairground waltzer, which was considered to be more realistic since it could be spun up and down, thus simulating a rocket flight from launch to landing. Volunteer test subjects proved than an astronaut could survive the g-forces expected from the first Mercury flights. But what of the effects of prolonged isolation during later flights?

Again, human guinea-pigs provided the answer. Airman Donald F. Farrell spent a week in an isolation chamber, then emerged into the world to face a barrage of pressmen and a handshake from Senator Lyndon B. Johnson.

Not surprisingly, the doctor reported that Farrell 'showed a deterioration from good spirits to the abrupt onset of frank hostility' but concluded that a space traveller could withstand prolonged periods of isolation inside a capsule no larger than a chicken coop.

Now that the question of survival had been answered to NASA's satisfaction, what sort of people should be selected? The general consensus was for military men, since they were used to following orders, no matter how suicidal they appeared to be. They were felt to be better equipped than civilians to face the physical stresses of rocket flight and the onset of 'frank hostility'. Best of all, for NASA's purposes, were jet pilots: small but wiry, used to high-speed flight, with all the required background in engineering.

So the Agency issued a prospectus for those with the right credentials: military test pilot, at least 1500 hours' flight time, good engineering background, under 40, less than six feet tall. Out of the hundreds of volunteers, NASA interviewed 69 and picked 32.

These sterling examples of American manhood were subjected to a bewildering battery of tests. There were personality tests, stress tests, tests of logic, of rational thought, of psychological suitability. The men in white coats had a field day. The prospective candidates had water pumped into their ears

(left) Mercury candidate Grissom endures the 'rotating equilibrium chair'; one of a bewildering battery of tests to prepare would-be astronauts for the rigours of space.

(right) Torture in the name of science: M. Scott Carpenter reads book, demonstrates sangfroid while enduring 130°F in NASA heat chamber.

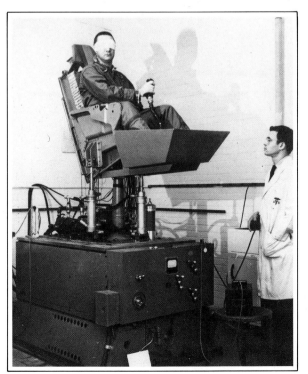

and electrodes rammed into their thumbs. They were asked to donate sperm, urine and fecal samples. They were given barium enemas, locked inside sensory deprivation chambers and whirled around in centrifuges.

On 2 April, 1959, the survivors made their debut in front of an excited Press audience. These were the Mercury Seven: Captain Leroy Gordon Cooper, Jr, Captain Virgil I. Grissom, Captain Donald K. Slayton (all Air Force); Lieutenant Malcolm S. Carpenter, Lieutenant Commander Walter M. Schirra, Jr, Lieutenant Commander Alan B. Shepard, Jr, (all Navy) and Lieutenant Colonel John H. Glenn, Jr, (the lone Marine).

The auditorium — NASA had chosen a ballroom next to the Agency's Washington HQ — was packed. The seven pilots were amazed to hear their names announced to rapturous applause from the world-weary hacks, many of whom were in tears. The next day, they woke to find themselves on every front page, TV show and radio news magazine in America. They had become instant heroes — the first stars of the space age.

The Sheiks of Space: Mercury 7 astronauts pose at desert survival school in casual attire — burnouses made from parachutes. From left to right: Gordon Cooper, Scott Carpenter, John Glenn, Alan Shepard, Gus Grissom, Walter Schirra and Donald K. Slayton.

Later that year, Mercury personnel at Cape Canaveral started working three shifts a day, seven days a week. The American attempt to put a man in space before the Russians was falling far behind schedule. The quick-and-dirty approach — using the available but low-thrust Redstone to fire an astronaut in a high arc over the Atlantic — was proving to be merely dirty. Lacking a big booster, Mercury was forced to settle for a capsule weighing little more than a ton. The final design was a bell shape, a bare six feet across. It was packed with instruments and life-support gear, into which a man was shoe-horned. The weight and size restrictions meant that every piece of equipment had to be small and light. It was like scaling down a sports car to the size of a child's pedal cart, and time after time the spacecraft designers went back to the drawing boards to shave an inch off here and a pound there. Another major headache was reshaping the Redstone, which had been designed as a battlefield missile, into a 'man-rated' rocket reliable enough to throw a human off the pad and into the skies without incinerating him.

Right in the middle of this engineer's nightmare came more news from Moscow. Khrushchev had pulled off another space spectacular. This time, the wily Soviets had sent an unmanned spacecraft in a graceful 300,000 mile loop around the moon, returning a single high quality TV picture of the dark side, which remained perpetually hidden from the sight of man. *Newsweek* called Lunik III 'the most impressive feat of the space age since the launching of the first sputnik.'

Again, the Russians demonstrated technical superiority: first the big rockets, now shooting the moon with a craft sophisticated enough to send TV pictures across the void.

Khrushchev made another propaganda point: the Russians named all the dark side features after Soviet heroes and landmarks — The Sea of Moscow, for instance — and US scientists would for ever more have to refer to them by their Russian names. The dark side of the moon was red. 'If we don't get going,' said a peevish US scientist, 'then there won't be any seas or craters left to name for Washington, Franklin, Edison, or anyone else.'

As America entered the new decade, there seemed little to show for the millions of dollars pumped into Project Mercury. The possibility of a launch by mid-1960 now appeared a mirage. Magazines ran articles like 'How To Lose The Space Race', and even one of the Mercury seven, those virtuous examples of American manhood, was quoted as saying 'I'll tell you one thing for damn sure. We'll get that first Redstone flight in the air before the end of 1960 if I have to light the match myself!'

Moved to reply to such flak, the boss of NASA, T. Keith Glennan, raised a protesting voice:

The Russians have exploited to the fullest the psychological, the political, and the propaganda possibilities. . . of their Sputniks and their Luniks. In the United States, our reactions have been violent, frequent, but of very short duration. In between the Russian firings, we have been preoccupied with the progress of the World Series. . .

Then he gave vent to an amazing piece of Cold War rhetoric:

We plainly must awake to the fact that the Russians would very much prefer to gain mastery of the world without having to fire a single ICBM; that they hope to become so superior in their scientific. . . capabilities that they will win world domination through industrial power rather than through shooting wars.

While Glennan raised the dreadful prospect of world domination through mastery of the heavens, NASA made up for the lack of space action by parading the Mercury seven around the country like a posse of film stars. Rights to their life stories were sold to *Life* magazine, and the astronauts' families were showcased as examples of Middle American wholesomeness.

Only one other person in the country was the subject of such admiring interest, and that was John Fitzgerald Kennedy, the Democratic contender for the forthcoming presidential election. Kennedy was emerging as the man of vision: an embodiment of youthful vigour who would lead America into the new dawn of the sixties. Compared to dour Ike, the retiring incumbent, and his shifty Vice-president, Richard M. Nixon — the Republican contender — JFK seemed to shine like a new star in the firmament. Eisenhower was still refusing to admit that there even *was* a contest with the Soviets, let alone that the US was losing it, a position which Nixon in turn defended. But Kennedy came straight to the point.

> We are in a strategic space race with the Russians, and we are losing. . . if a man orbits earth this year, his name will be Ivan. . . if the Soviets control space they can control earth. . . we cannot run second in this vital race. . . to insure peace and freedom, we must be first. . . this is the new age of exploration. . . space is our great New Frontier.

By the end of that year, NASA had chalked up some impressive successes: Pioneer V was sent towards Venus, setting up a record communications distance of over twenty-two million miles; a prototype weather satellite had sent down the first pictures of earth's global cloud layers; and President Eisenhower's voice had been bounced off a 100ft- diameter 'space balloon', Echo 1. Over on the West Coast, NASA pilot Joe Walker flew the X-15 past two thousand miles an hour and Major Bob White took it up to 136,000 feet, setting new speed and height records.

For the public, these space firsts were obscured by a series of Mercury disasters, the culmination of which was the 'popped cork' fiasco.

This happened one warm November morning in 1960 at Cape Canaveral. Five hundred dignitaries and pressmen gathered together to witness the first

Strelka and Belka, the first creatures to return, alive, from a flight round the world. 'When the Russian dogs bark, American politicians quake,' crowed Khrushchev.

The popped cork fiasco: Redstone engine fires — then abruptly shuts down — off goes the escape tower — and lands 1200 feet away, where bemused technicians ponder yet another disaster for Project Mercury.

test flight of an unmanned Mercury-Redstone system. The countdown went according to plan, the engine roared into life, and the mighty rocket lifted slowly off the pad. Then, as the startled audience gaped, the engine faltered and the Redstone settled comfortably back on to the pad again. There was a sharp report, and the escape tower flew off into the sky, just like a champagne cork. A tiny parachute opened, and the escape tower drifted away towards the nearby Banana River.

It was the nadir of Project Mercury. The national press ran articles with titles like 'How To Lose The Space Race', and the bewildered public wondered what had happened to the millions of dollars pumped into the effort to get an American into space. There might have been some consolation had they known that the Russians were also in trouble.

A month before the 'popped cork' drama, Nikita Khrushchev had stunned his audience at a United Nations Conference in New York. Sparks flew as the scowling Terror of the East pounded the rostrum with his shoe and gave vent to a barrage of anti-Imperialist invective. Even by UN standards, it was some show. Political commentators put Khrushchev's temper tantrum down to natural showmanship, but the real explanation was that the Soviet premier had just received word from home that not one, but two, attempts to send a spaceprobe to Mars had failed disastrously.

Every two and a half years, the relative positions of Earth and Mars enable spacecraft to cross from one to the other with the minimum use of fuel. Such a 'launch window' had opened during October, and Khrushchev wanted to take advantage of it. The propaganda value — announcing a successful voyage to the Red Planet — would be immense, particularly if Khrushchev was in America at the time. Oh, the humiliation! Oh, the superiority of the Soviet system under Nikita Khrushchev!

But the first Mars shot, and then a second attempt four days later, exploded high above Kazakhstan. Khrushchev said nothing, but waited until he returned to Moscow before venting his wrath.

The subject of Khrushchev's anger was Marshal Mitrofan Nedelin, head of the Soviet rocket forces and the man nominally in charge of space shots. What Khrushchev said to Nedelin was unrecorded and probably unrepeatable, but the Marshal was ordered to send a third rocket to Mars.

On the night of 24 October, Korolev's team raced against time to ready a semyorka before the last hours of the launch window ran out. At last, the giant rocket stood ready for ignition. Nearby, on a floodlit reviewing stand, sat Marshal Nedelin and his staff.

The countdown reached zero, and nothing happened. Marshal Nedelin ordered the launch crew to fix the live missile. Korolev and the others in the command bunker watched, horrified, as the gantry folded back against the rocket and the pad came alive with scurrying figures.

Nedelin ordered chairs to be set up near the rocket. There he sat, like an eastern warlord, surrounded by his staff, a few feet away from five hundred tons of rocket fuel. Suddenly, without warning, the engines burst into life. Held down by the gantry arms, Russia's third Mars shot exploded, blowing Marshal Nedelin, his staff and the launch crew to kingdom come.

Safe below ground, Korolev saw the detonation tear across the pad. Only one man survived — ironically, he'd sneaked into a shelter for a cigarette.

The catastrophe was never admitted. The members of the launch crew, the cream of Soviet rocket engineers, were given hasty funerals. Marshal Nedelin's death was announced 'in a plane crash'. His ashes were interred, with full military honours, in the Kremlin Wall.

On 12 April, 1961, just twenty days before the first scheduled Mercury shot, a 27-year-old Red Air Force pilot named Yuri Gagarin waved farewell to his launch crew and took the slow ride by elevator to the top of the Baikonur launch tower. It was early morning, and the day was crisp and clear. The winter snows had melted and flowers covered the steppe.

In the midst of this bucolic scene stood a bulky semyorka, mist-shrouded by liquid oxygen vapour from its fuel tanks. Hidden from the watchers on the concrete apron by the bulk of the launch tower, Gagarin was eased inside a large spherical cabin. The hatch was sealed, the launch crew made their way to safety, and the countdown began.

Then, as millions of Russians were about to start their day's work, the four arms of the launch tower unfolded like the petals of a flower, and the

Yuri Gagarin and mentor Sergei Korolev exchange farewells before launch. Gagarin, a young Red Air Force pilot, became the world's first spaceman, much to the chagrin of America. Handsome and personable, Gagarin headed the pantheon of Soviet space heroes.

Gagarin's moment of truth: 'I heard a whistling sound and an increasing roar. The giant spaceship began to quiver, and then slowly took off.

semyorka flamed into life. Gagarin felt the rocket shudder as it strained upwards — via the intercom, Korolev and the others in the control bunker heard him shout 'Let's go, let's go!' — and then the carpenter's son from a collective near Moscow was slammed into his couch by the acceleration as the rocket built up speed, heading for space.

Within minutes, Yuri Gagarin was arcing over the earth at 18,000 miles an hour, soaring into history as the first man in space, beating all height and speed records without effort. He was coasting along, a hundred miles above the Pacific Ocean, heading towards South America, exhilarated and in high spirits:

> I saw with my own eyes the spherical shape of the earth. . . the horizon is unusual and very beautiful. . . from the light surface of the earth to the blackness of the sky. . . The sun in outer space is tens of times brighter than here on Earth. The stars are easily visible. . . bright and distinct. The entire picture of the firmament has much more contrast than when seen from the earth.

He was fascinated by the absence of gravity:

> One's arms and legs weigh nothing. Objects float in the cabin. I did not sit on my chair as before but hung in mid-air. . . My handwriting did not change, although the hand did not weigh anything, but I had to hold the notebook, otherwise it would have floated away . . .

As he raced across the planet, the first spaceman could easily see the shores of continents, the islands, rivers and even the chequerboard farmland that lay far below him.

A hundred minutes after launch, the Vostok spaceship was approaching mother Russia and the period of maximum danger: re-entry, the flaming return to earth. Since no-one knew what to expect from the Vostock flight (some space doctors thought the ordeal of launch would render Gagarin senseless), Korolev had decided that the entire flight would be on autopilot.

Muscovites follow Gagarin's progress. Even Khrushchev was surprised by the spontaneous surge of patriotism that greeted the flight of Vostok 1.

Like their counterparts in the Mercury programme, the cosmonauts objected strongly to being mere passengers, especially since the autopilot on an earlier Sputnik test flight had flipped out and sent the ship with its cargo of dogs into a higher, and permanent, orbit. Korolev listened to the argument and conceded a certain amount of control to Gagarin: the manual controls would be locked up and the combination placed in a sealed envelope inside the cabin.

Gagarin did what any self-respecting pilot would do: not trusting his life to a machine, he unlocked the controls while the ship was over Africa and was ready to fly the ship himself. But his skills as a pilot were never needed. Right on time, the retro-rockets fired automatically.

> The Vostok began to lose speed. . . Then it began to enter dense layers of the atmosphere. Its outer surface heated rapidly, and through the portholes I saw the lurid crimson glow of the flames that raged around the ship. I was in a ball of fire plunging downwards. . .
> Weightlessness had long ceased, and the mounting overload pinned me to my seat. It kept increasing and was greater than during takeoff. The ship started to spin. . . But the spinning, which worried me, soon stopped, and the rest of the descent went normally.

One hundred and eight minutes after liftoff, the first man into space was swinging on the end of a parachute above a cow-pasture near the village of Smelovka, watched by a cluster of startled peasants. (The capsule was too heavy for a parachute landing, so Gagarin had ejected at twenty thousand feet.)

Meanwhile, the entire Russian nation was jubilant.

Shortly after Gagarin had taken to the skies, Moscow Radio interrupted its normal programme with a blast of patriotic music, followed by a simple announcement: 'The world's first spaceship with a man on board has been launched in the Soviet Union on a round-the-world orbit.'

Public transport halted so that passengers could listen to public-address speakers. Factory workers turned off their machines. Schoolchildren, shopworkers, farmers, office staff — all huddled around radio sets to tune into the news of Gagarin's progress through the heavens. When the terse announcement came that the cosmonaut had landed safely, the party started. All Russia took to the streets to celebrate.

Return to earth: the charred shell of Vostok 1. Soviet officials insisted that Gagarin landed inside the capsule, thus qualifying for the 'first spaceman' title under international rules. In fact, he ejected and landed by parachute. To the Russians, propaganda was more important than truth.

Khrushchev, of course, used the occasion to bait the Americans. 'Let the capitalist countries try to catch up with our country, which has blazed the trail into space. . .' he crowed.

Then came the special-edition newspapers with blazing red banner headlines; the triumphant return to Moscow; the parades of singing workers; the official reception in Red Square (televised live and relayed, for the first time ever, to Western Europe); the presentation of medals; and the placing of Gagarin at the head of the pantheon of Virtuous Soviet manhood. Khrushchev made a speech comparing the cosmonaut to Columbus, then awarded Gagarin at the head of the pantheon of virtuous Soviet manhood. Khrushchev made a speech comparing the cosmonaut to Columbus, then awarded with the honour of being the first spaceman. Of Korolev, there was no mention.

The reaction of Americans to Gagarin's flight was a mixture of gloom and bitterness. They hated having to play second fiddle — especially to the Russians. It was even suggested in some quarters that Gagarin's flight was faked, or that he was the first *surviving* cosmonaut, the others having perished in space during re-entry. The latter theory was to remain in circulation for years after, but it was never proven.

The news hit Washington early in the morning, and as the day drew on the right people said the right things: President Kennedy congratulated the Russians, the head of NASA congratulated the Russians. Behind the gracious façade, fury at the propaganda defeat rose.

Down at the Cape, Project Mercury was buzzing like a hornet's nest. 'We could have done it a month ago if somebody at the top had simply decided to push it,' cursed one worker. 'All of us were longing for someone to say "OK boys, let's go"' cried another. The feeling was that bureaucratic sloth had prevented them: 'If Columbus' *Santa Maria* had been handled that way, she would never have left the harbour.'

Three weeks after the flight of Yuri Gagarin and nearly a year behind schedule, Project Mercury was ready to launch its first astronaut. It was not a propitious time: America was stunned by the Bay of Pigs affair, and two Mercury test shots, using the big Atlas booster, had been aborted in mid-flight.

It was a clear day at the Cape. Before dawn, Lieutenant Commander Alan B. Shepard Jr, US Navy, clad in a silver spacesuit, squirmed into a tiny Mercury

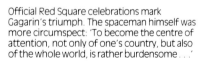

Official Red Square celebrations mark Gagarin's triumph. The spaceman himself was more circumspect: 'To become the centre of attention, not only of one's country, but also of the whole world, is rather burdensome . . .'

capsule and prepared for launch. He was still there four hours later, as engineers wrestled with a score of minor problems.

Despite the hundred and one simulations, tests, and dry runs, the spacecraft designers had neglected to provide Shepard with the means of relieving himself. America's first space hero was about to pee in his pants.

Shepard was not amused. The capsule was hot and cramped, there was barely enough room for him to waggle his toes, and there he was, lying on his back with his feet in the air on top of an eight-storey-high bullet. At one point he threatened to come down and fix the Redstone himself.

Finally the countdown reached zero, the Redstone engine ignited, and Shepard lifted slowly to the sky.

'And riding with him,' gasped an awed *Time* magazine reporter, 'was his country's pride, the prestige of his country's science, the promise of his

After four uncomfortable hours, Shepard finally takes to the Florida skies atop von Braun's Redstone booster.

Alan Shepard, in pre-launch test, is shoe-horned into his tiny Mercury capsule as America prepares, once again, to follow the Soviets into space.

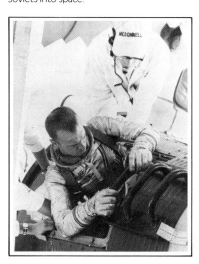

country's future on the expanding frontiers of the universe.'

The first American astronaut made a flawless, if brief, journey into space. The big booster shot Shepard in an arc over the Atlantic, landing just 300 miles down-range from Cape Canaveral. Shepard had barely five minutes of weightlessness as he came over the top of the hundred-mile-high curve. The whole flight lasted just fifteen minutes — peanuts compared with Gagarin's grand orbit — but when Shepard was winched out of the sea, every American from the President on down thought he was the greatest.

Except for the Russians. Gagarin was quoted as saying: 'We sent some dogs up and down, just like Alan Shepard.' Now it was Khrushchev's turn to feel chagrined, since Shepard's cannonball ride gained such worldwide publicity.

Never before had science met showbiz: schools were named after Shepard (it was suggested that his home town should be renamed 'Spacetown USA'). Mayor Wagner of New York promised the returned hero the biggest ticker-tape parade in the Big Apple's history, and the Mayor of Los Angeles immediately tried to outbid New York.

The new space hero was immediately invited to the White House for a hand-pumping, medal-pinning ceremony with the new President. Behind the glitter of the occasion, Kennedy was weighing up the next move.

His advisers had given him two options: abandon the race with the Russians in favour of a low-key satellite programme in which man would be relegated to the role of bystander; or go for broke and embark on a space project of such overwhelming ambition that every Russian success from Sputnik to Gagarin would be eclipsed.

Such a project was already in the pipeline. It involved sending a man to the moon, and NASA dubbed it Project Apollo (the image of the god Apollo riding across the heavens was thought to give the best flavour to such a grand undertaking). Though the Agency, presenting the scheme to Eisenhower at the White House, compared a lunar voyage to Columbus' discovery of America, Ike was not impressed. Referring to Columbus' patron, Queen

At the end of his 'cannonball run', Shepard exits capsule. Said Gagarin: 'We sent some dogs up and down, just like Alan Shepard.'

Isabella of Spain, he quipped 'I'm not about to hock my jewels to send men to the moon,' while one of his cronies retorted 'This won't satisfy everybody. When they finish this, they'll want to go to the planets!' The White House unbelievers roared with laughter at such an outrageous idea.

As Eisenhower's successor, however, Kennedy was convinced that space was a symbol of the twentieth century, and was more receptive to NASA's lobbying. On the day of the Shepard reception new NASA boss James Webb and Secretary of Defense Robert McNamara submitted a report in which they argued:

> It is man, not merely machines in space, that captures the imagination of the world. . . Dramatic achievements in space symbolise the technical power and organising capacity of a nation. . . The non-military, non-commercial, non-scientific but 'civilian' projects such as lunar and planetary exploration are, in this sense, part of the battle along the fluid front of the Cold War.

Within two weeks, Kennedy had decided that he would go for broke and back Apollo.

'Now is the time,' he told a packed and star-struck Congress,

> 'to take longer strides; time for a great new American enterprise. . . I believe this nation should commit itself to achieving the goal, before this decade is out, of landing a man on the moon and returning him safely to the earth. . . No single space project in this period will be more impressive to mankind . . .

There wasn't a dry eye in the house. The idea had clicked. It was simple and breathtakingly spectacular. Beat the Russians to the moon! Regain national pride!

Mindful of the strength of feeling after Alan Shepard's flight and the presence of national TV, Congress voted its approval with the people's bucks. Dollars were showered like confetti upon the bewildered space engineers. For the first year alone, NASA was given over one and a half billion dollars: the boomtown era of space travel had arrived.

As if to confirm the new mood of confidence, the second Mercury flight, with Virgil 'Gus' Grissom at the controls, went like a dream. The only jarring note came at splashdown.

America's first star of space meets the First Family. Kennedy offers congratulations to Shepard on White House lawn. Onlookers include Jackie Kennedy (left) and Shepard's fellow Mercury astronauts.

Grissom survived the hardships of blast-off and re-entry, only to have the capsule sink under him when the hatch cover blew prematurely. America's second astronaut was left floundering helplessly in the Atlantic while the rescue choppers hovered overhead. By the time he was winched up, Grissom was half-drowned, but the Agency PR men cheerfully glossed over the incident. Nothing would be allowed to tarnish the image of man and machine in perfect harmony.

NASA had now put two Americans into space on Redstone rockets. Neither flight was as spectacular as Gagarin's, but they were enough to show that the US meant business. This mood — of satisfaction if not of euphoria — was not to last. Within three weeks of Grissom's up-and-down shot, Korolev sent a second Soviet cosmonaut around the world.

This time, Gherman Titov stayed aloft not for one orbit, nor three (the duration of the proposed Mercury-Atlas shots) but seventeen. The flight lasted an entire day. Much to the consternation of the military, Titov zipped over the United States three times, in a clear demonstration of Khrushchev's ability to rain H-bombs down on the defenceless Americans.

Gus Grissom survives space only to face death at sea: rescue helicopter hooks onto capsule — capsule sinks, leaving Grissom floundering — Grissom is winched out of water like a drowning rat.

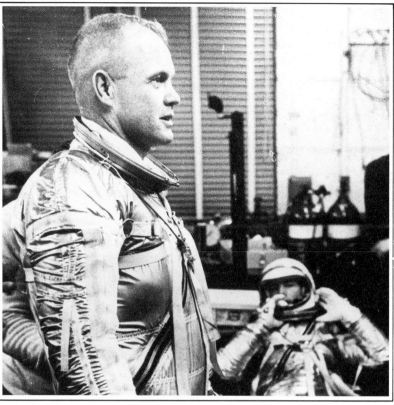

The Lone Marine: John Glenn, at attention, prepares to do battle with the Russians and restore America's fading self-image.

The Russians later admitted that Titov suffered from nausea during the flight — again raising doubts about the ability of the soft human frame to withstand the rigours of space travel —but Titov landed safely on Soviet soil, neither insane, riddled with meteoroids, nor splattered over the cabin walls.

Again, by demonstrating that a cosmonaut could survive for at least a day, Khrushchev had scored another propaganda point. Titov's day in space forced NASA to drop the planned third Mercury-Redstone shot and go for a convincing display of American prowess: a flight round the world.

The pilot was to be Colonel John Herschel Glenn Jr. of the US Marines. Unlike Shepard and Grissom, Glenn had already made his mark on an image-conscious public long before his Mercury shot. He had flown in both the Second World War and the Korean War, and then made headlines when he flew one of the hot new jet fighters on a supersonic coast-to-coast run.

Glenn embodied all the Middle American virtues. He was devoutly religious, didn't drink, smoke or curse and ran two miles before breakfast every morning. Raised in the mid-west, Glenn had a homely freckled face and was at ease with the press and the public. Even though some of the other Mercury pilots regarded Glenn as a humourless jock, his public image was so informal that he even appeared on a TV quiz show, **Name That Tune**, and walked off with the top prize.

After the inevitable countdown holds and delays, Glenn rode the Mercury-Atlas through a flawless launch as 135 million Americans sat transfixed in front of their TV sets. He had little sensation of speed. Like Gagarin, he simply felt he was flying along in an airliner. Weightlessness was no problem, enjoyable even, and the sunsets were unbelievable:

As the sun goes down, it's very white, brilliant light, and as it goes below the horizon you get a very bright orange colour. Down close to the surface it pales out into a darker blue, and then off into black . . . if you've been out in a desert on a very clear, brilliant night when there's no moon and the stars just seem to jump out at you, that's about the way they look...

Going into the first of his three nights, Glenn was intrigued by thousands of tiny points of light — like fireflies he said — which appeared to surround the capsule. He thought they might be the remains of a bizarre Air Force experiment in which 350 million copper needles were shot into space, never to be seen again. But when Glenn later described the 'fireflies' to a NASA psychiatrist, the shrink merely drawled: 'But what did they say, John?'.

Towards the end of the first orbit, the Mercury capsule — Friendship 7 — started veering wildly. Glenn took over the controls from the Mercury autopilot, and all seemed well. But minutes later, launch control at the Cape picked up a signal that the heatshield was loose. This meant real trouble: if the signal was correct, John Glenn was heading for a fiery death over the Atlantic. NASA's first round-the-world flight was turning into America's first space drama.

While ground control was biting its collective nails and wondering how to get Glenn down alive, the astronaut in question was having a fine time flying his ship. After all, John Glenn was a test pilot, not a monkey.

Friendship 7's tendency to tumble was due to a combination of defective thruster and wandering gyroscope. The latter determined the correct attitude of the capsule, then ran that information through a black box. The black box issued orders to the thrusters, which fired tiny bursts of gas in sequence until the ship was correctly lined up. Glenn, by taking manual control of the thrusters, was playing cat-and-mouse with the gyroscope. The process was not only personally satisfying to Glenn; it also proved to the disbelievers on the ground that man was an essential part of the Mercury system, and not just a passenger.

NASA public relations portrays astronauts as clean-living, healthy examples of American manhood. Glenn (right) and Carpenter in 'beach boy' pose.

Glenn on Broadway. Adulatory crowds — the biggest in New York's history — welcome the returning hero: John Glenn, first American to orbit the earth. Later, Glenn capitalised on his flight to become first, a Senator, then a candidate for the Democratic Presidential nomination.

But while Glenn was enjoying himself, no-one at ground control was having fun. After analysing the heat shield signal, the Mercury engineers concluded that it was probably erroneous. Since there was no way they could confirm this, the Cape changed the plans for re-entry.

To get back down from orbit, ground control would fire a set of braking rockets. These retrorockets sat in front of the heatshield, held to the capsule body by three metal straps. After firing, the retros would be jettisoned, leaving the heatshield to bear the brunt of re-entry. Ground control now wanted the retros to stay fixed to the capsule, reasoning that the straps might hold the heatshield in place. The qualifier was 'might' — it was essentially a gamble.

John Glenn was coming to the end of the third and final orbit, jinking Friendship 7 around with the thrusters to line it up for the critical re-entry angle: if he made it too steep, the capsule would burn up; if it were too shallow, he would miss the landing zone and end up in the middle of Africa. He'd run a test on the heat shield switch and felt reasonably confident that the problem lay with the circuitry, not the shield. But he wasn't a hundred percent sure either. So he stayed cool, braced himself for the shock of re-entry, and fired the retros.

'It feels like I'm going clear back to Hawaii,' he radioed, as the g-forces hit him, then Friendship 7 fell like a stone. Glenn saw a red glow outside the window, and flaming chunks of debris as big as a man's fist flew past. The heat shield was breaking up.

Down on the ground, the heat of re-entry had knocked out communications with the capsule, so there was no way of knowing whether Glenn was alive or had been reduced to charred carbon.

Then the radio crackled. It was Glenn; he'd made it — the flaming chunks were the remains of the retrorockets, not the heat shield. 'Boy, that's a real fireball,' he whooped. The Cape went wild.

Out in the Atlantic, a Navy destroyer plucked Friendship 7 from the water. Glenn clambered out of the capsule and, with the entire ship's crew cheering and shouting, a rating followed Glenn across the deck, painting his footprints white. The Returning Hero! The New Lindbergh! Even his footprints were preserved for posterity.

CHAPTER THREE

THE COLD WAR WARRIORS

THREE MONTHS after Glenn's flight, Scott Carpenter became the second American to ride a Mercury capsule around the world. Handsome, with the physique of a bodybuilder and a reputation as a superb athlete, Carpenter was the complete astronaut: a veritable Captain America of the skies.

But as the earth rolled by beneath him, Scott Carpenter became so absorbed in pitching the capsule around for a better view that he squandered most of his fuel and, despite ground warnings, was late in firing his retro-rockets. A hundred miles below him, the Mercury engineers watched aghast as Carpenter wobbled in over the horizon. During the radio blackout which accompanied re-entry, a tearful Walter Cronkite flashed the news to the nation: 'We may,' he choked, 'have lost an astronaut.'

The 'lost' astronaut explains what really happened. Carpenter at debriefing: he would never fly in space again.

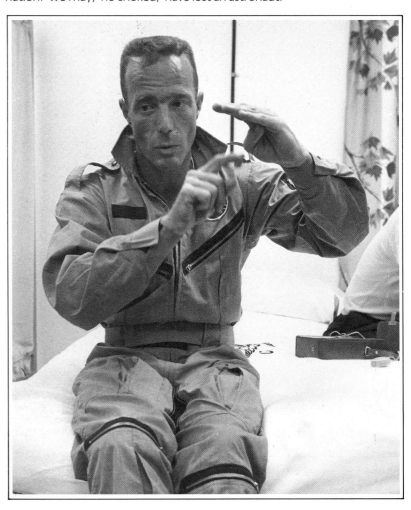

'No-one could strip an astronaut of his glory . . . they were right up there with the gods . . .' Scott Carpenter and family pose with Kennedy in the White House.

Then came the good news. Carpenter was 250 miles off-course, but safe. When the rescue planes turned up, they found Scott Carpenter floating happily on his raft, completely and blissfully unaware of the drama back home.

That was the beginning and end of Scott Carpenter's career as an astronaut. In test-pilot parlance, Captain America had 'screwed the pooch'. He'd committed the unforgivable sin of losing control of the spacecraft and ignoring ground warnings. Captain America was an astronaut in disgrace.

Scott Carpenter's fall from Olympia was, in the eyes of NASA alone, a purely internal matter. There was no court-martial, no public humiliation. Even within the Agency, it was never openly discussed. It was just assumed that 'the sonofabitch will never fly again'. For the public, though, not even the President himself could strip a Mercury astronaut of his glory, no matter how seriously he'd screwed the pooch. The 'Mercury 7' were sitting right up there with the gods: they could do no wrong in the eyes of America.

Nevertheless it looked as though the US was at last catching up with the Russians. Following Carpenter's flight, a NASA pilot pushed the X-15 rocket

'Heavenly Twin' Nikolaev in zero-g training for the first cosmic formation flight — a flight that struck terror in the hearts of the US establishment.

plane past 4000 mph, almost as fast as Alan Shepard's sub-orbital ride. A few weeks later, millions of TV viewers on both sides of the Atlantic tuned into the first 'live via satellite' broadcast. Relayed by Telstar, the pictures were blurred and the sound faint, but the message was clear: communications satellites could bridge continents at the speed of light. Distance was no object: Telstar could bounce a phone call from New York to Paris as easily as it could relay a message from Manhattan to the Bronx. The global village was just around the corner.

Since Titov's flight, NASA and the US military between them had launched over thirty satellites and spacecraft: the Russians had put up just eight. But soon the new mood of quiet confidence was shattered.

On 11 August, 1962 the Soviet Union successfully launched a Vostok spaceship crewed by Major Andrian Nikolaev. A day later, timed to the very second, Lieutenant Colonel Pavel Popovich took off from Baikonur on a trajectory that allowed him to cross Nikolaev's path. The two cosmonauts stayed up for three and four days respectively, passing within a mile of one another — the first cosmic formation flight.

Moscow TV ran live coverage of the cosmonauts, showing them apparently at ease in their weightless world. These live-from-orbit shows were accompanied by biopics of other Russian heroes. The deathbed scene of one such pioneer dissolved into a shot of semyorkas roaring into the skies, while a choir sang the Russian spacemen's song:

> I believe, my friends,
> That caravans of rockets
> Will speed us from star to star. . .

It was, said *Time* magazine, 'a variety of corn that would have made a second-rate Hollywood puff merchant blush.' The entire Soviet media went to town: newspapers printed pictures of the cosmonauts with their families on the beach, or swimming, or sniffing flowers. Press releases emphasised the common touch of the cosmonauts, both of whom were peasant sons. Popovich cuddled a cloth Lenin doll, while Nikolaev asked the ground for the latest soccer scores. The 'heavenly twins' were just ordinary Russian lads.

Both men landed safely. Nikolaev's widowed mother was pictured sobbing with joy, handkerchief at mouth, at the news of her son's safe return. The cosmonauts made a tearful reunion, and burst into song before taking the congratulatory phone call from Premier Khrushchev.

Then came the triumphal return to Moscow. Wearing full dress uniform, the heavenly twins stepped out of the airliner at Vknuvo Airport, and made

'Paternal Gaze'. At Moscow rally for Nikolaev and Popovich, Nikita Khrushchev smiles benevolently over cosmonauts' families.

their way down a red carpet into the open arms of Khrushchev and the entire Presidium. The twenty-mile route into Moscow was lined with cheering crowds, young women pelted the motorcade with flowers, and a full 21-gun salute greeted them as they entered Red Square, where, next to a beaming Khrushchev, Nikolaev described the flight as 'one more vivid proof of the superiority of socialism over capitalism.'

Back in the West, Sir Bernard Lovell of Jodrell Bank Observatory claimed that the flight of the heavenly twins had put Russia so far ahead 'that the possibility of America catching up in the next decade is remote.' NASA officials told a crowded press conference that things would get worse before they got better, and predicted that Russia would probably win the race to send a man around the moon. The only way to catch up, they suggested, was to pump more money into the American space effort, which was already financed to the tune of five and a half billion dollars a year.

They were joined in the demand for increased finance by the generals, ever eager to raise the spectre of Soviet domination of the heavens, and hence earth. 'If the Russians can send Colonel Popovich up to look at Major Nikolaev, they can go up and look at one of our birds,' argued one Pentagon official. 'Why, they could knock out our satellites by hitting them with almost anything!'

This allusion to the vulnerability of the growing fleet of US spy-in-the-sky satellites was followed by a deluge of dire predictions: orbital H-Bombs capable of laying waste to entire cities; manned space interceptors to blast intruders out of the heavens; 100-mile-high command posts to direct orbiting battle fleets; defensive screens of satellites armed with the offspring of the new laser technology.

'We cannot rule out the possibility that Russia can orbit satellites with 100-megaton hydrogen bombs over our heads,' a USAF general declaimed. 'We can't take chances. The sooner we get manned space stations operated by military men, the better off we will be.'

The Russians refused to take at face value the implication that they were about to turn space into a battleground. It was all an American plot to justify the Pentagon's own plans for the military conquest of the heavens, they claimed, and a Soviet general indicated that the Kremlin would respond. 'It is perfectly clear that if the imperialists continue to conduct research into means of using cosmic space for military goals, then the interest of guaranteeing the security of the Soviet state demands definite measures from our side.'

In the midst of these nightmare visions of celestial mayhem, Wernher von Braun tried to put the flight of the heavenly twins into perspective. The Geman rocket chief, now working on the massive Saturn booster that would eventually propel Americans to the moon, pointed out that his rival Korolev, while displaying great skill and competence, had used the same booster and spacecraft that had taken Yuri Gagarin into orbit. The Vostoks of Nikolaev and Popovich were fired into similar orbits, but had no ability to change course or link up. True rendezvous in space, and with it the ability to inspect or destroy American satellites, was still a long way off.

'Y'all ought to quit messing around with space and watch TV like the good Lord intended for people to do,' he was told, in no uncertain terms, by one taxpayer, evidently unimpressed by his calming words.

While the histrionics raged, NASA fired Mariner 2 towards Venus, mysterious planet of love, shrouded in clouds which even the most powerful of telescopes could never penetrate. Ever since the time of Galileo, Venus had touched the imagination of scientists and poets alike. What lay beneath the clouds? A prehistoric swampland of dinosaurs and giant ferns? A planet-sized ocean inhabited by fishmen and sirens (described by one wit as 'oceans of soda-water, but nothing to mix with it')? Or even a lost civilisation of advanced beings privy to the secrets of the universe? Fishmen! Dinosaurs! Intelligent reptiles! Superbeings!

During its 109-day journey, the robot explorer survived power failures, collisions with cosmic debris and severe overheating. Then, as it came within twenty thousand miles of the planet's cloud-tops, Mariner 2 sent back the first close-up information on another planet: a surface temperature around the melting point of lead.

As the engineers and scientists whooped with relief, poets and sci-fi writers felt cheated. Mariner 2 had wrenched the veil from Venus' face, but the sight was not a pretty one. The temperature of melting lead! No water! No steamy swamps! No fishmen! No superbeings!

Worse was yet to come. The clouds were revealed as a mixture of hydrocarbons, a vast planet-sized pollution zone. Smog! Not a tropical greenhouse, but the greenhouse effect! Venus was just like Los Angeles, only hotter!

It was a great victory for American science and technology, but a defeat for the imagination. As the poets slunk homewards, the UFO fraternity who

Schirra rides the Atlas booster, *en route* for the 'textbook' Mercury flight.

believed in the superbeings fought a desperate rearguard action: the Venusians had captured Mariner 2 and were feeding it with false information.

Ten weeks after the heavenly twins, and almost five years to the day since the flight of Sputnik 1, Walter M. Schirra made what NASA called 'the textbook' Mercury flight.

Schirra did everything right: conserved fuel, made a perfect re-entry after six orbits and splashed down within spitting distance of the recovery ship. All was not lost.

There was now only one Mercury flight on the cards, and the original seven astronauts had been joined by the 'next nine', a new cadre in training for the Gemini series planned for the middle '60s.

Gemini would do more than go up, circle the earth a few times and then come down. It was a two-seater 'space taxi', with enough power, fuel and oxygen for an extended stay in orbit, and it slotted right into NASA's game plan for landing a man on the moon.

The Agency had sold Kennedy the Apollo project; now they had to figure out exactly how to do it. The first option was to fire a massive rocket direct to the moon, land and take off again. This was called 'direct ascent', and after the engineers had done their calculations they realised it was pure sci-fi. There was no way they could build a big enough booster. The second option was to manufacture a space station in earth orbit, where space riggers would manufacture a moon ship from parts sent up from earth. This was dubbed 'assembly-in-orbit', and it too was rejected. The engineers finally settled, after much argument, on a third approach.

The idea was to fire two spacecraft into earth orbit on a single big booster — a mother ship and a small lunar lander. While in earth orbit, the three-man crew would waltz the lunar lander around to the front of the mother ship, dock the two together and use the mother ship's engine to propel both craft into orbit around the moon.

Once in lunar orbit, two crew members would clamber into the lunar lander, detach it from mother (leaving the third crewman to maintain a lonely vigil above the moon) and drop down to the lunar surface. If all went well, they would fly the lander back up, dock with the mother ship, discard the lander and head for home.

This way, NASA could reduce the total weight of a moon flight and use the new Saturn booster which von Braun's rocket team was building. Like Sergei Korolev's semyorka, Saturn used a cluster of engines to generate millions of pounds of thrust, and it was the principal reason why von Braun had been transferred to NASA. Saturn had no military application, and it was the first purely civilian booster to be developed by the US.

The engineers had the theory and the booster, but they lacked the

Downtown Houston, home of the astronauts, turns out to acclaim Schirra.

technique. Apollo required true piloting skill: the crew would need to dock, undock, fly around and redock. There was no way a computer could handle the complexities of an Apollo flight. It needed the firm touch, the cool judgement, the perfect timing of a true space ace. And all NASA had done so far was to send a few test pilots around the world.

So the Agency came up with Project Gemini. Aboard Gemini, the pilot would be king. He would have computers and radar to assist him, but they would be mere tools at his command. Gemini pilots would actively fly the spacecraft towards an unmanned target and dock with it, undock, change orbit and do all the things required on an Apollo flight. True space flying! Buck Rogers for real!

On 15 May, 1963, Gordon Cooper made the last Mercury flight.

That morning, long before sunrise, Cooper took the elevator to the top of the Atlas booster and squeezed into the tiny Mercury capsule, whereupon (to the astonishment of the launch crew) he promptly fell asleep.

Here was America's last Mercury astronaut, sitting on top of two hundred thousand pounds of volatile rocket fuel, waiting to be thrown into the hostile no-man's-land of space, calmly pushing out z's.

Off went Cooper into the sky, and for eighteen orbits everything went as planned: 'Working just like advertised,' he drawled.

Cooper, like Scott Carpenter, enjoyed running through the science

Gordon Cooper prepares for his day in space — a flight to compete with the Russians on their own terms.

experiments, which many of the astros regarded as 'Larry Lightbulb' stuff which only interfered with the pilot's main mission of flying the ship.

During a sequence which included a test of the astronaut's ability to pick out details of the landscape unfolding far beneath him, Cooper swore blind that he could see objects as small as trucks on a highway. Some of the scientists down at mission control thought he was hallucinating ('first he falls asleep, now he's seeing things!') but later flights confirmed that astronauts could indeed see with incredible clarity.

On the nineteenth orbit, Faith 7's electrical system started shorting out. By the penultimate orbit, number 21, the short had started a series of malfunctions that blew carbon dioxide back through Cooper's helmet, messed up the life support system and knocked out the autopilot.

As every light on the mission consoles flashed from green to red, Cooper took over manual control of Faith 7 and prepared to hurtle back through the stratosphere.

The odds were stacking up against him. Faith 7's last orbit was a night-time pass, the autopilot was crocked, every instrument in the capsule was throwing hysterics, and Cooper was taking in great wafts of poisonous CO_2.

With the cool and judgement of a true follower of the Buck Rogers tradition, Gordon Cooper lined Faith 7 up for the critical re-entry angle, held the capsule steady, fired the retros on the second, flashed into dawn high

The end of Project Mercury. Cooper, with the odds against him, flies back to earth for a perfect touchdown and now awaits the recovery team.

over the Pacific, crossed the US in a ball of fire and made a perfect touchdown.

Hail the returning hero! NASA was elated. Cooper had notched up enough points to put America well and truly back into the space race.

Following the success of the heavenly twins, Korolev was looking towards a flight that would answer, once and for all, the question 'Can man survive in space'. This was to be a seven-day marathon, during which flight doctors could assess space sickness, fatigue, the effects of zero-g and the host of other factors which could influence a long space flight to the moon or an extended stay aboard a space station.

Korolev's careful presentation fell on deaf ears. Khrushchev was in no mood to approve such a flight. The Soviet Premier wanted to hear of spectaculars, stunts, front-page news; something which would take the heat off his feud with Mao Tse-Tung. The Chinese leader was a thorn in Khrushchev's side, threatening to break the Sino-Soviet alliance and split world communism. Khrushchev, essentially a pragmatist, had little time for the dogmatism of Mao, who accused him of spawning a cult of personality, of being a fourth-rate political hack and (this last deeply wounding Khrushchev's vanity) of

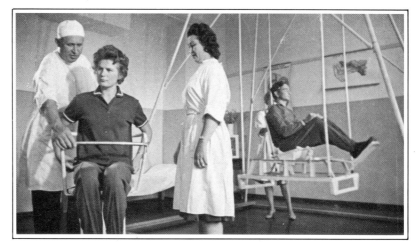

Spacewoman Tereshkova (seated) in training.

'Valya', the former textile worker, about to join the male preserve of space.

having nothing to do with the successful Russian space programme.

There was also the question of Khrushchev's succession. Who would be the next party boss? A strong candidate was Leonid Brezhnev, a loyal Party man under Stalin, whom Khrushchev had plucked from obscurity and boosted

The world's first spacewoman autographs her landing capsule.

through the Politburo. Like his mentor, Brezhnev had built up an impressive power base and was awaiting an opportunity to go for the jugular.

Korolev was told to plan another circus, and in the summer of '63 the world learned of another Soviet space first. This was another double act, a dual Vostok flight, but with a difference. Vostok 5 carried Colonel Valery Bykovsky into orbit, where he was joined by Vostok 6, whose pilot was a woman!

What a coup! The world's first spacewoman, and she was a Russian! Brilliant! What a stab in the vitals for the macho image of the Mercury 7, the supermen of America!

'A brilliant star has flared up in the cosmic firmament,' exulted *Tass.* 'It outshines all the film stars in the world. Never and in no country did women ever attain such height.'

And out came the life-story: 'Valya' was a textile worker, an accomplished parachutist and a prominent member of the Young Communist League; in short, an ordinary Russian girl. In Khrushchev's Russia, anyone could go into space, a point that was not lost on many Americans. 'The Russians have proved to us that you don't have to have twenty years of test-pilot experience before you can handle one of these capsules,' said the chairman of the Senate Space Committee.

The sentiment was echoed by American feminists. Said Clare Boothe Luce: 'We must stop trying to make paper dolls out of our women.' Jane Hart, fighting to have women astronauts accepted by NASA, agreed. 'I'm tempted to go out to the barn and tell the story to my horse and listen to him laugh,' she said.

After three days in orbit, more than the total spent by all the Mercury astronauts put together, Tereshkova made a triumphant return to earth. Following the traditional Moscow welcome, she toured the world — including the US — was made a high-ranking member of the Committee of Soviet Women, and became an ambassadress-at-large and a shining example of the

(left) Khrushchev shares a joke with his cosmonauts after 'Valya's' flight. Gagarin and Tereshkova flank Nikolaev as the canny Soviet Premier basks in their reflected glory.

(right) Russia's new royalty. Khrushchev toasts bride Valentina and groom Andrian. Their wedding was Moscow's event of the year.

emancipation of Soviet women in the Khrushchev era.

Six months after the flight, Valya married Andrian Nikolaev, the only bachelor spaceman and coach to the women cosmonauts. It was the social event of the Moscow year. Tereshkova, two months pregnant, walked down the aisle on the arm of Nikita Khrushchev. He reportedly grinned from ear to ear the whole day, as well he might. The Soviet Premier had again manipulated the Russian space programme for his own political prestige.

But despite Tereshkova's successful flight and the long tradition of women aviation pioneers, twenty years would pass before another woman flew in space. The idea of women muscling in on the exclusive male preserve of space flight upset many of her cosmonaut colleagues. It ruined the image of the Soviet supermen. A year later, her husband articulated the mood:

This kind of work is tough. The mission programme makes big demands on her, especially if she is married. So nowadays we keep our women here on earth. We love our women very much; we spare them as much as possible. However, in the future, they will surely work on board space stations, but as specialists — as doctors, as geologists. . . and of course, as stewardesses.

It was a statement the Mercury 7 would heartily agree with. Mikhail Sholokhov, author of **And Quiet Flows the Don**, went even further: 'A woman in space! Say what you will, this is incomprehensible. It contradicts all my set conceptions of the world and its possibilities.'

1963 marked the end of both the Mercury and Vostok series. Both spacecraft were single-seaters, with simple navigation equipment and no means of changing orbit or manoeuvring around in space. They were merely means to send a man, or woman, up into space and back down again. The new generation of spaceships would be more sophisticated. NASA was building Gemini, a two-seater 'space taxi' for launch in 1964. Gemini would be sent aloft by a booster a third as powerful again as the Mercury-Atlas combo, and would be packed full of high-technology wizardry which included computers, radar and lightweight spacesuits for the crew. It would fly dockings, spacewalks and long-duration missions — up to fourteen days — and then return to earth with pin-point accuracy. (It was even planned to sling a Gemini capsule beneath a Rogallo Wing, or paraglider, for a 'soft' touchdown on land. The idea was later dropped, but it started a new sport: hangliding.)

The Soviet space team under Korolev was planning its own sophisticated two-seater: a big, roomy spaceship with braking rockets to lessen the final impact so that the crew could land inside the capsule rather than by parachute. This craft, the Soyuz, wouldn't be ready until 1965 at the latest.

Faced with the threat posed by Gemini, Khrushchev concocted yet another stunt to upstage the Americans. If the US planned to send two men into space, Russia would send a three-man crew around the world. This was to be the biggest Russian gamble so far.

Korolev was ordered to take out the ejection seat and the reserve parachute from a surplus Vostok. The parachute was replaced by a small rocket engine, timed to fire ten feet above the ground. To save weight, out went the rocket pack that would hurl the Voskhod, as it was re-named, away from its Semyorka should the booster misfire.

There was now room for three men — but not their bulky spacesuits. Were the potential dangers not so great, the plan would have been almost comically inept: three astronauts in a capsule built for one, with no spacesuits or emergency escape system, with enough oxygen and supplies for a minimum stay in space. If they survived all that, the crew would have to wait until the last second to find out whether they would be heroes or dogmeat. It was a space project with absolutely nothing going for it other than as a pure propaganda stunt.

On 12 October, 1964, the seventh anniversary of Sputnik, three men in a

Voskhod blasted off into orbit. Only one, Colonel Komarov, was a pilot. The others were Boris Yegorov, a physician and Konstantin Feoktistov, the designer of the Vostok conversion: an assignment equal to sending the designer of the Titanic on its maiden voyage. They spent an uncomfortable day in space, then landed safely. Feoktistov had done his job well.

Khrushchev had pulled off his most risky space spectacle yet, but he was in no position to reap the rewards. While the three cosmonauts whirled nervously around the world, the Soviet Premier had been deposed by his former protege, Leonid Brezhnev. The intrepid cosmonauts knew nothing of this. They chatted briefly with Khrushchev via a radio link from his Black Sea holiday home, and that was the last they heard from the man who had gambled so recklessly with their lives. When Komarov asked for a 24-hour extension — the limit of their oxygen supplies — Korolev quoted Hamlet: 'There are more things in heaven and earth, Horatio, than are dreamed of in your philosophies' and promptly ordered them back.

Instead of the traditional Moscow reception, the bewildered cosmonauts spent the next few days in quarantine near the landing site. It was a week before the three space heroes entered Red Square. The huge portrait of the Premier had vanished, and instead of a beaming Khrushchev they were greeted by a new face, that of Premier Brezhnev, who had saved his official coming out for the cosmonauts' welcome. Brezhnev hugged them, then spoke his first words as Premier to the waiting crowd. Not once did he mention Khrushchev.

Ironically, the man who had made the heavens his own personal fiefdom had been toppled from power during his greatest escapade.

Five months after the downfall of Nikita Khrushchev and five days before the first Gemini flight, Pavel Belyayev and Alexei Leonov rode the second Voskhod into orbit.

The two men were more fortunate than the previous Voskhod crew — they had at least been afforded the luxury of wearing spacesuits — but the flight was still a gamble. It had been planned by Khrushchev before his fall from grace, but his Brutus, Brezhnev, was not so proud as to refuse to take the honours from his predecessor. This time a surplus Vostok was modified to carry an airlock, through which Leonov was to exit the spaceship and try for the world's first spacewalk. Both men knew that an unmanned test shot the

'Why do the Russians always beat us to the punch?' complained one American on learning that Alexei Leonov (here exiting Voskhod) had become the world's first spacewalker. Yet again Russia was in the lead — though at some risk to the cosmonauts.

month before had proved a disaster, but political considerations outweighed caution. Upstaging Gemini was the name of the game as far as the new Soviet bosses were concerned.

The flight went flawlessly. Within an hour Leonov was strapping on a portable oxygen rig and readying himself to leave the womb-like safety of Voskhod 2. Belyayev inflated the airlock — a tough plastic tube — and pressurised it. By a combination of floating and crawling, Leonov inched his way out of the Voskhod and into the tunnel, where he paused to check his suit and oxygen supply. Then he cracked open the oxygen valve, inched open the outer hatch and slowly floated out into space, tethered to Voskhod 2 by a thin safety line.

He curled and tumbled lazily in space, performing a slow-motion gymnastic show for the benefit of the TV camera perched on Voskhod's hatch. What an experience, to be the first human earth satellite! It was like a dream sequence, as the continents, oceans and cloudscapes floated beneath his feet.

Leonov's meditations were rudely interrupted by the discovery that returning to Voskhod 2 was in no way as easy as leaving it. Try as he might, he couldn't get his legs back inside the airlock: the high pressure of his suit prevented him from bending at the waist. He was in deep trouble.

Inside the Voskhod, Pavel Belyayev heard his partner gasping with exertion. As Leonov's pulse rate hit the danger line, Belyayev knew he was starting to panic. There was nothing Belyayev could do. Leonov had the only suit and oxygen backpack, so a rescue was out of the question. Leonov was on his own.

Outside the capsule, Leonov realised that his life depended on reducing the suit pressure, making it flexible enough for him to jack-knife into the tunnel. Depressurisation virtually guaranteed an attack of the bends, the deadly build-up of nitrogen in the bloodstream which afflicts deep-sea divers. The future for Alexei Leonov did not look promising. He either waited outside the capsule until his oxygen ran out, which would be fatal but painless, or he risked an agonising death inside the airlock.

Leonov took the risk. As the suit deflated, he deftly hooked his feet around the lip of the tunnel, elbowed his way inside and dogged the hatch. Half dead from exhaustion and fear, he was back inside the spaceship. Just ten minutes had elapsed since he left Voskhod 2.

But the crew's troubles were not yet over. On the seventeenth and final orbit, Voskhod 2's autopilot ran amok and refused to line the ship up for the critical re-entry path. Belyayev cancelled the retrofire sequence, took over manual control and flew Voskhod 2 around for a second try. The extra orbit meant they were behind schedule and well off-course, but Belyayev did his best to control the tricky capsule as it skidded back through the atmosphere.

Belyayev and Leonov landed in the remote wastes of the Ural Mountains, two thousand miles away from Kazakhstan. Now they had more problems. Despite all the marvels of twentieth-century technology, Belyayev and Leonov faced a predicament that had confronted countless generations of travellers: they were snowbound in the middle of a dense pine forest, with no food, no source of heat, and no means of transport. Since an antenna had snapped off during re-entry, they had no radio. Leonov had cheated death in space only to become marooned on earth.

The two space heroes spent an uncomfortable afternoon in the snow, still clad in their bulky spacesuits to keep out the cold. Come nightfall, huddled up to a tiny fire, Leonov spotted a hungry wolf-pack nosing around the treeline. That was enough for the intrepid duo. They beat a hasty retreat back inside the capsule, where they stayed all night, kept awake by the sounds of snapping and snarling from beyond the hatch.

Early the next morning, a ski patrol came upon the heat-scarred Voskhod capsule sitting in a marsh of melted snow. Out popped two dishevelled and half-crazed Soviet space heroes, and they roundly cursed the astonished troopers, the Politburo, Sergei Korolev and the entire Russian space programme.

CHAPTER FOUR

RIDING THE FIRE

O
N THE morning of 23 March, 1965, Gus Grissom and John Young flew the first Gemini spaceship into earth orbit. The event had been overshadowed by Alexei Leonov's spacewalk the previous week but, after all, this was just a test run. The headline-hitting Gemini flights would come later.

Gus Grissom was about to rack up a personal first as the only American to make a second spaceflight. His partner was a rookie, as was the Titan II-Gemini combo they were sitting on.

Beneath them was fourteen stories of booster which, like Redstone and Atlas, was a modified Air Force long range missile. Titan was designed to sit inside a deep concrete silo hardened against Russian attack. Instead of the kerosene-liquid oxygen mixture of Atlas, the Titan ICBM burnt what the engineers called 'exotic' fuel which could be stored inside the missile's tanks while it sat underground, waiting for doomsday. Titan was simple, reliable (so the two astronauts hoped) and powerful. The first stage alone packed nearly half a million pounds of thrust — the combined power of some thirty thousand family cars.

If the Titan was open to superlatives, so was the two-seater Gemini capsule. Though it superficially resembled the bell-shaped Mercury capsule from the outside, under its skin Gemini was a different beast altogether.

The crewmen sat inside a compartment scarcely larger than the interior of a two-seater sports car. Surrounding them were switches, toggles, dials, displays, lights, joysticks, buttons and enough hi-tech hardware to fill an electronics showroom. Instead of the tiny Mercury hatch, there were two batwing doors. Each pilot could see out through a porthole, which the crews liked to think of as a windscreen, and rested on contour couches strapped to rocket-powered ejection seats.

Behind the crew compartment was a section containing the retrorockets; behind that an 'equipment module' which housed communications gear, fuel tanks, fuel cells for electricity, and the all-important thrusters.

Gemini may not have looked like a classic sci-fi spaceship, but it was designed to behave like one. Its onboard computer would give the crew instant readouts on course, velocity and direction; its radar the precise location and range of a target ship; its banks of thruster rockets the power and manoeuvrability to zip around in space with the facility of a stunt cyclist.

The powerful Titan booster took off so smoothly that Grissom and Young had to check the instrument panel to confirm they were in the air. Five minutes away from the pad, Grissom kicked in Gemini's engines to place them on a near-perfect course. For the second time, Gus Grissom was in orbit.

He had dubbed his Gemini 'Molly Brown' after the 'unsinkable' heroine of a Broadway play. This ironic reference to his earlier Mercury flight did not find favour within NASA. Only when Grissom revealed his second choice — the 'Titanic' — did the bureaucrats grudgingly consent.

Around the world sailed Molly Brown, with her crew alternatively bitching about the science experiments they had been asked to carry out and praising the craft's agility.

By the end of the short flight, Grissom had changed Molly Brown's orbit, direction and course — all under manual control. No longer would American

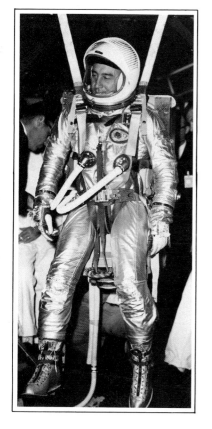

The new space era: Gus Grissom hangs from his straps while awaiting his second spaceflight and the first in America's new two-seater Gemini spacecraft.

Grissom and Young endure the onset of
nausea as 'Molly Brown' wallows.

The long wait. McDivitt and White, suited, sit
patiently through the final preparations for
their flight into earth orbit.

astronauts be mere passengers in a robot capsule. From now on, they would
be true space pilots.

Again under Grissom's control, Molly Brown arced back into the
stratosphere. For the second time, Gus Grissom found being in space
preferable to the hazards of earth: Molly Brown hit the water so hard both
men pitched into the windshield. Battered and bruised, they endured thirty
nauseous minutes inside the suffocatingly hot spacecraft. This time, there
was no way Grissom was going to crack the hatch open before the pick-up
team arrived.

The next Gemini flight marked the turning point in the fortunes of America
in space. It was planned as a four-day marathon, with the added attraction of a
spacewalk.

There were dire predictions about the effects of both the spacewalk and
the duration of the flight. NASA knew from the Russians of Leonov's
problems. Disorientation outside the capsule was no joke: it raised the spectre
of a wild terror-crazed astronaut going into convulsions beyond all hope of
rescue. Four days in space, the longest-ever US flight, was another unknown.
Some flight surgeons feared that after the return to earth, the crewmen
would at best become basket cases or, according to an even gloomier
prognosis, maybe even die from the terrible effects of zero gravity.

It was thus a very popular flight. A thousand newsmen descended on the
new NASA command centre at Houston, Texas, while hundreds more
crowded onto the viewing stands at Cape Kennedy. Another reason for the
popularity of Gemini 4 (Molly Brown was officially Gemini 3, the first two shots
being unmanned tests) lay in the fact that both crewmembers were young
and good looking. Jim McDivitt and Ed White had known each other since
college and had been in the same class at test pilot school. White, upon whose
head the spacewalk laurels would rest, was the personification of the John
Glenn clean-cut all-American astroboy: a tall, handsome West Point graduate
in his early thirties.

And here were the two buddies, riding the Titan to the edge of space, about
to embark on America's most spectacular and risky venture since Alan
Shepard's first Mercury flight.

After a delay of only an hour, the Titan booster made a flawless liftoff in
front of a live-via-satellite TV audience. Space travel was becoming
operational. Three times around the world they went, and then Ed White was
ready for the walk in space: suited, hooked up with air hoses, clipped to a
tether and eager to crack the hatch.

The task proved more difficult than anticipated. It took some mighty
wrestling and hammering to budge White's door open, and then suddenly

there he was, floating slowly out of the spacecraft. Unlike Leonov's Voskhod, there was no separate airlock to be negotiated — White simply pushed gently against his ejection seat to obtain enough leverage to exit from Gemini 4, then used a zip-gun powered by compressed oxygen to propel himself to the end of the tether.

Ed White performed somersaults, body turns and played around until the zip-gun ran out of fuel, while the other half of the cosmic duo snapped away with a hand-held camera. The fifteen minutes in outer space were too short for White, who was now playing at 'walking' across the panorama beneath him. 'In deference to the President,' he joked, 'I avoided stepping on Texas.'

Ground control finally ordered him back inside. 'It's the saddest moment of my life,' he complained, feeling neither disorientated nor spacesick. Returning to Gemini 4 was no problem. White pulled on his tether and floated towards the spaceship. When he was within range, McDivitt caught hold of his legs and gently eased him back inside.

Closing the hatch was an exhausting chore. By the time White had locked it into position, sweat was streaming down his face and he was completely exhausted. McDivitt immediately powered down the ship and the two men tried to get some sleep. They still had three days to go.

The flight plan called for the crew to sleep alternate periods in case of emergency, but in the cramped confines of the Gemini capsule it was difficult for the man on watch to avoid disturbing his partner. Every few minutes the autopilot would fire a thruster to keep the craft on station, and then there was constant radio chatter from ground control. A Gemini spacecraft was no place for getting a good night's sleep.

For the remainder of the flight, McDivitt and White drifted through space.

'Please, Ed, get back in the spaceship,' pleads Ground Control as White swims happily over the planet.

Like all good tourists, they spent much of the time taking pictures of the earth rolling below them.

Around the fifty-orbit marker, Gemini 4's onboard computer quit on them. Now was the chance to test out the 'piloted spaceship' concept, whereby a man could fly Gemini without benefit of ground or computer. McDivitt took over the controls while White ran instrument checks and called out velocity and attitude numbers. All the way through re-entry, the two men chatted away, checked the dashboard instruments and enjoyed the scenery.

Gemini 4 cleaved the skies over Texas, left a sonic boom over the Deep South and splashed into the grey Atlantic waters. After they were fished out and placed gently on the deck of the rescue carrier, White did a little war-dance of victory. They'd lost a little weight, but no more. After four days and one spacewalk, Ed White and Jim McDivitt had come through with colours flying and faces grinning.

President Johnson came to Houston to glad-hand the intrepid duo, a million-strong crowd turned out to greet them in Chicago, and NASA sent them to meet Yuri Gagarin at the Paris Air Show. There was more jubilation to come. NASA's Mariner 4 made the first successful reconnaisance of Mars, the red planet, which like Venus had excited the imagination of generations of poets and astronomers. Earthbound telescopes could detect frost-covered polar caps (water?), dark regions (vegetation?) and mysterious markings that crisscrossed the planet (canals?). Maybe it all added up to evidence of some ancient planet-wide civilisation (Martians!).

Mariner 4's pictures showed no canals, its instrument readings no water. Mars was a planet that had seen better days, an arid cratered wasteland with an unbelievably thin atmosphere. No Martians! Not even evidence that there had been, millions of years ago. Again, science had triumphed over romance.

Having proved to the satisfaction of everyone except the most doom-laden flight doctors that a crew could survive four days in space, NASA planned to send the next Gemini astronauts on another marathon. This time it was to be eight days aloft: the duration of an Apollo moon flight.

Gemini 5 blasted off from Cape Kennedy on 21 August, 1965, carrying Mercury veteran Gordon Cooper and his rookie partner, Pete Conrad. Their unofficial motto was 'eight days or bust'. NASA, ever mindful of political caution, refused to endorse the byline in case they did bust. But everyone on the operational side of Gemini — the engineers and technicians who liked to refer to themselves as 'the guys in the trenches' as opposed to the politicos and bureaucrats at the Agency HQ in Washington — heartily agreed with the sentiment.

Cooper was more receptive to science than his 'fly the ship and damn the eggheads' test-pilot brethren, hence the Gemini 5 schedule was packed with civil and military science experiments. Most of the time, however, Cooper and Conrad just drifted along in space. Come the eighth day, Cooper barrelled back in, landed the ship and racked up another cosmic milestone. Their worst problem had been boredom: both men were in great shape, if groggy and fatigued. After just two flights, the bogey of weightlessness was beginning to fade. Space was beginning to lose its terrors: the unknowns were slowly becoming known.

For the first time, it seemed, America had caught up with the Soviets in the race for the heavens. From Cape Kennedy, mission control at Houston, the world-wide network of tracking stations and recovery ships, the hundreds of thousands of scientists, engineers, technicians, doctors, specialists, computer jockeys to the robot spacecraft, the man-rated rockets and their superhero crews, the great NASA machine was replacing the fantasy world of Buck Rogers and Dan Dare with the reality of space travel. Fact was fast outstripping fiction.

With Gemini three-for-three, NASA was going for the big one: rendezvous in orbit.

The idea of two ships meeting and mating in space was always taken for granted in sci-fi films: space pilots from Buck Rogers to Han Solo merely pressed a few buttons, pulled back on the joystick and hit the brakes. In reality, to locate, catch up and synchronise course with a target the size of a small truck in the wastes of space was a task requiring precision equipment, calculations so complex only a computer could handle them, and the highest flying skills. Not only was rendezvous in orbit an essential first step towards the goal of landing a man on the moon, but it would also determine whether the glorious future of astronauts making routine flights to and from space stations was possible or strictly for the sci-fi writers.

The flight plan for Gemini 6 called for the ship to rendezvous and dock with an unmanned target, Agena. This was a modified upper stage of the type used to launch a hundred satellites. The front end formed a collar into which the nose of a Gemini would slot, while the aft section was essentially a powerful rocket engine to be used as a booster system for later Gemini flights: a space tug for the space taxi.

Since the development of Agena had been plagued with problems, NASA called for Gemini 6 to rendezvous, dock and detach without firing Agena's big engine. This was reckoned enough for one mission.

On 25 October, the crew of Gemini 6 watched and waited as Agena and its Atlas booster were prepared for launch. As soon as the space tug was successfully placed in orbit, Mercury veteran Wally Schirra and co-pilot Tom Stafford would themselves roar into space on a catch-up trajectory, then use Gemini's thrusters to effect the rendezvous.

Off went the Atlas. Minutes later, the Agena target cut loose from the big booster, fired its own engine, and promptly disintegrated. Scrub the mission! With no target vehicle, there was little point in launching Gemini 6. Schirra and Stafford's hopes of a flight into space had fallen apart before their eyes.

There seemed little anyone could do except wait for another Agena to be readied, an operation that could take months, but in the midst of this gloom and despondency two engineers at the Cape came up with another solution: why not use another Gemini as the target? There was no way the two spacecraft could dock, but they could fly in formation — not miles apart like Popovich and Nikolaev, but a matter of feet, near enough for the two crews to eyeball each other.

The idea had been proposed before and turned down. There were just two many unknowns and, besides, it was reckoned that Korolev had used two launchpads for the flight of the heavenly twins. There was only one available for Gemini.

In the aftermath of the exploding Agena, rapid-firing two Geminis looked better. The engineers went to work. In just three days, the Gemini team brainstormed through the problems, convinced the NASA hierarchy, and won permission to fly to the first true rendezvous between manned spaceships.

The new plan involved merging the Gemini 6 mission with that of Gemini 7, in which Frank Borman and Jim Lovell would spend two whole weeks in space. Gemini 6 would be put together on the pad, checked out and stripped down again. The 7 would be set up, checked out and fired. There would follow a race against the clock to set up and fire Gemini 6 on a catch-up trajectory.

Less than six weeks after the Agena disaster, and only four years since Yuri Gagarin completed one lonely lap around the world, Frank Borman and Jim Lovell lifted smoothly into the Florida sky on the beginning of a fourteen-day space marathon. 'We're on our way, Frank!' shouted Lovell.

Out on the edge of space, Borman cut Gemini 7 loose from the big booster and flew alongside it as the spent Titan tumbled lazily in the bright sunlight. Then Borman kicked in the thrusters and they coasted into orbit, leaving earth behind them.

Back on the ground, Kennedy engineers went into overdrive to prepare the pad for Gemini 6. The system was working like clockwork — just eight days after the 7 ship had taken to the skies, Wally Schirra and Tom Stafford were riding the elevator to the top of the launch tower.

Gemini 6's countdown reached zero, a massive gout of flame cascaded into the concrete spillway. . . and abruptly died. Something had killed the engines.

For the first time, two American astronauts were stranded on top of a cocked and deadly rocket, faced with the choice of either punching out on their ejection seats or facing fiery death. There were 150 tons of rocket fuel beneath them, and according to the cockpit instruments the Titan was a few inches above the pad. If the instruments were true, within a fraction of a second the Titan would fall back, rupture and explode.

At this point, according to the rule book, Schirra should have punched them out and away from the smoking rocket.

But Schirra kept his cool. He knew the Titan hadn't moved, and he was trusting his own senses against the instruments. He just sat there, doing nothing. After the smoke had cleared, there was the Titan, sitting safe on the pad.

If the 6 crew had punched out, they risked severe injuries from the force of the ejection rockets and the parachute landing. Had Schirra's judgement been wrong, there would have been no second try.

'I've never been more scared in my life than during those few seconds when we didn't lift off,' he said later. 'If that booster was about to blow, there was no choice. It's death or the ejection seat.'

They were now back to square one. Gemini 7, their 'friendly target', was up in space with only six days to go.

The Cape engineers worked a 24-hour shift to strip Titan's engines down and find the fault. The answer came in the early hours of the next morning: someone had left a dust cover inside a fuel pump. The lives of two men and a hundred million dollars' worth of hardware had been placed in jeopardy by a piece of plastic worth a few cents.

On 15 December there were two days left to chalk up the first space rendezvous. At 8.30 in the morning, the countdown again reached zero: 'For the third time, go!' screamed Schirra, willing the rocket to move. Again the clock started, but this time the great rocket shook and shuddered. They were on their way at last.

Minutes later, the Gemini 7 crew, flying over the African coast, saw the speeding contrail of the 6 ship coming up towards them. Borman and Lovell were having a fine time aloft. Both were in good shape after 11 days in the cramped capsule, and they were looking forward to seeing the 6 crew.

The latter were trailing them by 1000 miles at the end of their second orbit. Over New Orleans, Schirra started the first of a dozen thruster firings that would hopefully put them next to Borman and Lovell. Three hours into the flight, the 6 crew was within radar range of Gemini 7; two hours later, they were near enough to pick out their target's running lights in the darkness. Schirra was taking it slow and easy (his motto was 'always take an even strain') with deft touches on the controls. Another hour passed and they were within a half mile of the target, still in the earth's shadow.

Then, as Schirra and Stafford came out of darkness, they saw Gemini 7 in front of them, only a few hundred feet away, glowing like an arc light in the fierce sunshine. Schirra crept up on Borman and Lovell like a cat stalking a bird, firing bursts from the forward thrusters to cancel his velocity. They were about a hundred feet apart, and there was no relative motion between the ships. It was the world's first space rendezvous — two spacecraft were floating along, side by side, high above the cloud tops.

Down at mission control, Houston, they cheered, stomped, waved flags and lit up cigars. Wally Schirra had beaten the Russians to the big one! Buck Rogers for real! A true space pilot!

Up above them, America's latest space hero played cosmic tag with his 'friendly target'. The onboard computer had helped them reach Gemini 7, but now it was strictly by eyeball: man was flying the machine. They closed to within a foot of the gleaming 7 ship, and then the fun started:

Schirra and Stafford on their way at last, heading for space and a rendezvous with Gemini 7.

'We felt like a terrier playing with a bone,' said Schirra. 'We were nibbling at them, and I must admit it was fun.'

The 6 crew peered in at the bearded faces of Borman and Lovell a few feet away, who in turn were fascinated by the fireworks of their visitors' thrusters and slightly alarmed by the long tongues of flame that lapped out towards them. For a while they coasted nose-to-nose, then Schirra peeled off, flew around Gemini 6 and handed the controls over to Stafford, who went through his own stunt-flying routine.

They finally settled in 'for the night' ten miles apart, still within eyeball range. Every thirty minutes or so, the sun would flash above the horizon and bathe them in searing light. Half an hour later, they were in the twilight zone, watching the sun cast an orange tint over the cloud banks before dropping below the edge of the earth. Then they were alone, with only the running lights of their partner ship for company. Occasionally they would see a burst of flame and sparks in the distance as the ship's autopilot kept it steady. Otherwise they were alone, hanging between the bright, steady stars and (if the skies below were clear) twinkling patterns of city lights far below.

After the hours of concentration and effort, Gemini 6's crew were tired and hungry. They tucked into the peanut cubes, dehydrated main courses of

Two spacecraft floating along, side by side, high above the cloud tops — Gemini 7 from 6.

sausage patties or chicken and freshened up with damp washcloths — the nearest anyone in space could come to taking a shower. They fell asleep immediately.

Come next morning (NASA tried to keep some temporal continuity by running spacecraft on Houston time to avoid upsetting astronauts' biological clocks) the crew of Gemini 6 prepared for landing. They'd accomplished everything on the flight plan. Besides, Schirra had caught a bad head cold and was glad to be going home. With Schirra on harmonica and Stafford on hand bells, they serenaded the 7 crew with an appalling rendition of 'Jingle Bells' and made their goodbyes. 'We'll see you on the beach' drawled Schirra, then flipped Gemini 6 blunt-end forward, released the equipment section and started the clock for re-entry.

Coming down through the atmosphere, Schirra sloughed off some of his speed by using the blunt heatshield to lift the capsule back towards space, skipping up and down like a cosmic surfer. The technique was vital for an Apollo crew coming back from the moon, and it also gave Schirra the ability to control his landing. This he did, dropping Gemini 6 within ten miles of the waiting recovery ships and TV cameras. It was the first televised 'live' splashdown.

With their visitors gone, Borman and Lovell maintained a lonely vigil high above planet earth. The novelty of space travel was beginning to wear thin: 'We had peaked up for the rendezvous,' said Lovell. 'Now Wally and Tom were back on the carrier, and we were still sitting here having our problems.'

On this, the thirteenth day in space, Borman and Lovell had lost two of their thrusters, they were low on gas, one of the vital fuel cells was on the blink and ground control kept bombarding them with new experiments.

Despite the flight ruling that one pilot must be suited at all times, both Borman and Lovell were stripped down to their longjohns — the only way they could cope with the oppressive heat of the tiny, cramped and sweaty spacecraft cabin. They read books and listened to piped music and daily news bulletins from the ground. When told of a collision between two airliners over New York, Borman remarked 'It looks like it's safer up here than down there.'

Retorted Lovell: 'We're not down yet, buddy.'

Finally, a week before Christmas Day, it was a time to clean up the cockpit, make an awkward scramble into their bulky pressure suits, and prepare for return to earth. Ground control asked if they wanted to take dexedrine pills to make themselves more alert for the re-entry. Borman replied that he wasn't sure he could stay in the same cockpit as Lovell if his partner took one.

After 330 hours and five million miles, the crew of Gemini 7 waited in darkness over the Pacific. It was an apprehension shared by all astronauts and cosmonauts.

'If you have an accident in an airplane,' mused Lovell, 'something's going to happen, you hit something, or it blows up. In liftoff and re-entry, a space vehicle is like an airplane. Something's happening. But if the rockets fail to retro, if they fail to go off, nothing's going to happen. You just sit up there and that's it. . . You know that you have 24 hours of oxygen, 10 hours of batteries, and very little water.'

To their relief, the retros fired on time, punching the two astronauts back into their couches. Lovell felt he was being dropped inside an inkwell: the darkness outside was total. The onset of g-forces, the first they'd felt for fourteen days, felt like a ton, but the crew was too busy trying to get near to the recovery carrier to worry. Borman, the command pilot, had bet Wally Schirra they'd land nearer to the carrier. He won his bet, beating the Gemini 6 crew by less than a mile. They were stiff, weary and generally beat, but they were down, alive and fit enough to amble across the carrier deck. Borman and Lovell had faced the unknown terrors of weightlessness for two weeks and survived.

Borman (right) and Lovell; bearded, scruffy and happy. They had faced the terrors of weightlessness and survived.

The medics were perplexed. The post-flight examination showed that Gemini 7's crew were in better shape than Cooper and Conrad. In some unknown manner, their bodies had apparently adapted to the rigours of spaceflight.

If the medics scratched their heads and puzzled over the unexpected findings, NASA was jubilant. The news that humans could adjust to the strange domain of space was a boon for Project Apollo and a bonanza for the concept of a manned space station in which crews would spend weeks, not days.

It was a great Christmas for NASA. America had finally caught up with the Russians by way of a string of glittering successes. The future looked bright.

Just two weeks into the new year, 1966, a sombre obituary in **Pravda** reported the death of Sergei Korolev. It was now the turn of the Soviet Union to taste the bitter pill of defeat along the hazardous route to space.

Korolev was 59 when he died on an operating table in Moscow, the victim not only of a legacy of hardship in the Gulags but also of a blunder by his surgeon, the Soviet Health Minister. What started as a simple operation for haemorrhoids ended with Korolev lifeless from internal bleeding. The man who had virtually single-handedly directed the great Russian space spectaculars of the 50s and 60s, who had sent the Red Star of Soviet Russia into space, who had driven his rival Americans to impotent rage and depression with one Sputnik after another, whose fleet of R-7 rockets had given the people of the West nuclear nightmares, was gone, and with him went part of the Soviet dream of the conquest of the heavens.

Ironically, his state funeral in Moscow, attended by cosmonauts and Party officials, was the first time many in the West learnt of his identity. Korolev's achievement as the first czar of outer space had been as the anonymous Chief Designer, a man with neither a face nor name, who was just another cog in the Soviet machine.

Sergei Korolev had spent the last year of his life trying to make good the mistakes of Khrushchev, whose appetite for the spectacular had come near to wrecking the Soviet space effort by focussing its scarce resources on manic one-off propaganda stunts. Korolev must have followed the deliberate progress of Gemini with envy, knowing that he was lucky to get the two Voskhod crews back alive. He had no follow-on programme to Voskhod, and no booster, as yet, to replace the ageing R-7.

So Korolev had gone to his new boss, Brezhnev, seeking patronage to rebuild the cosmonaut cadre and design a new spaceship and a more powerful booster rocket. The tables were turned: it was now the Russians who needed a crash programme to challenge America's lead in space.

No sooner had the ashes of Sergei Korolev been set in the Kremlin Wall than the Russians landed Luna 9 on the moon and received the first pictures from the surface of that inhospitable world. Next, two dogs were sent around the world for three weeks, landing safe and sound on Russian soil. Then came disaster. A test launch of Korolev's new booster, the Proton, ended with the giant rocket exploding high in the stratosphere. Sergei Korolev had been dead only eight weeks. It was a bad omen, especially since his old rival Wernher von Braun had just successfully test-fired the first Saturn, forerunner of the big rockets that America would use to land a man on the moon.

It was at this time, early in 1966, that tragedy also struck the Americans. The crew scheduled for Gemini 9, Charlie Bassett and Eliot See, were killed when their T-38 jet fighter crashed into the McDonnell Douglas plant at St Louis. It was the second astronaut fatality: Ted Freeman, a close friend of Bassett, had been killed two years earlier when a goose crashed through the windshield of his T-38. He was 38, Charlie Bassett just 34.

Their deaths were chalked up to 'attrition' : 'In a business like this,' said a NASA spokesman, 'you've got to expect losses,' but it was a grim reminder of the risks involved in the space race.

Out of the cadre of 36 astronauts recruited for Mercury, Gemini and Apollo, there were only 28 left. Some, like Scott Carpenter, had been gently eased out, others had voluntarily left the group because of marital problems, an inability to fit in or medical reasons. Of the original Mercury 7, only Cooper, Grissom and Schirra were still available to fly. Both Shepard and Deke Slayton, the one who never made a Mercury shot, had been grounded by the medics. The rate of attrition was high.

The Gemini 6-7 rendezvous paved the way for more spectaculars, and more moments of high drama. Five months after Schirra and Stafford had been left at the starting gate, Gemini 8 roared skywards to dock with a waiting Agena target. Neil Armstrong, a civilian NASA pilot who had logged some great runs in the X-15 rocket plane, gently nudged Gemini 8 into the nose of Agena.

'We are docked,' Armstrong reported exultantly, 'and he's really a smoothie.' Congratulations on this, the first time two spaceships had joined in orbit, were premature: while Armstrong and his partner Dave Scott checked out the Agena, their combo went into a tumble. Armstrong punched in Gemini's thrusters and backed off from the space tug, but the trouble got worse.

'It's in a roll,' he radioed, 'and we can't seem to turn anything off,'

They were inside a three-ton catherine wheel, rolling 60 times a minute. The crew got dizzy, their vision was blurred, and they couldn't focus on the instruments. No matter how many buttons they pressed, nothing happened.

Down on the ground, it seemed to have the makings of a disaster. Agency top-brass were called out of meetings and ferried by plane and siren-screaming motorcade to Houston and the Cape. Millions of Americans, tuning into radio and TV, listened and watched in amazement as NASA's normally unflappable 'voice', Paul Haney, shakily announced that the flight was in danger.

By now, all the manoeuvring thrusters were running on empty. The only way to dampen the roll, caused by a jammed-open thruster, was to use the re-entry control rockets. Armstrong cut them in, and still nothing happened. He flipped toggles, threw switches — and then they fired. Slowly Gemini 8 came out of the roll.

'OK, relax,' said a relieved Mission Control, 'everything is OK.'

But it was not. Fail-safe flight rules dictated that, if the re-entry thrusters were used, a crew must get down fast. If anything went wrong and the Gemini 8 crew found there wasn't enough fuel left in the manoeuvring thrusters to hit the initial re-entry angle, they would either burn up or disappear into space.

So the flight was scrubbed. Armstrong and Scott made an emergency

return to the Pacific Ocean some 700 miles from the coast of Japan and floated disconsolately while they awaited the recovery team.

Four months later, Tom Stafford and Gene Cernan waited their turn to dock with an Agena space tug. This was the ill-fated Gemini 9 flight, whose first crew, See and Bassett, had 'bought the farm' in St Louis.

The Agena, powered by its Atlas booster, rose two hundred thousand feet, pitched over in a nosedive and headed back towards Cape Kennedy like a runaway express train.

By the time Gemini 9 finally took to the skies to chase a compromise target (another Agena couldn't be found in time) Tom Stafford had been left on the pad no fewer than six times. His frustration was compounded when he found they couldn't dock with the target — its shroud was firmly jammed over the docking port. Then, to make things even worse, Gene Cernan's spacewalk was cut short after his faceplate fogged over. Like Leonov, Cernan found spacewalking a lot more difficult than the simulations had predicted.

Gemini 9 had not been a lucky flight.

Finally, in the high summer of 1966, John Young and Michael Collins made it up to their waiting Agena, docked, and for the first time fired the space tug's big engine.

Young and Collins were facing Agena when the engine lit off. Young described what happened:

> There was a big explosion. We were thrown forward in the seats. Fire and sparks started coming out of the back end of that rascal. The light was something fierce, and the acceleration was pretty good. . . The shutdown was just unbelievable. I never saw anything like that before, sparks and fire and smoke and lights.

Gemini 10 coasted over the top of a 500-mile high arc, further into space than any ship had ever been. The view from that height was disappointing, since the bulk of Agena blocked most of their view. Young described it as 'just like backing down the railroad track in a diesel engine looking at a big boxcar in front of you.'

Young fired the engine again, changing the elliptical orbit back to something like a circle, dropped off their Agena and caught up with the 'dead' Agena of Armstrong and Scott. Collins floated over to inspect it, found few problems with the unfamiliar territory and effortlessly racked up another US spacewalk success.

Less than three months passed before Pete Conrad and Dick Gordon took the high road into space. Again they locked onto an Agena tug, but this time Gordon spacewalked out onto the nose of Gemini 11 and rode the combo bareback. 'Ride 'em, cowboy,' chortled his partner from inside the cabin. As Agena's engine roared into life, Conrad yelled, 'Whoop-de-doo! That's the biggest thrill of my life.' Up and away they went, 900 miles out from earth, watching as the horizon receded like a great round ball, and wondering whether they would ever stop racing out into space. The only sour note in the flight came when Gordon spacewalked, ran out of time, and retreated exhausted to the safety of the ship.

On 11 November, 1966, two astronauts shuffled up the ramp towards their waiting Titan booster. On the back of his pressure suit, each carried a sign: 'The' and 'End'.

Together they were about to embark on the twelfth and final Gemini shot. They were James Lovell, who had already racked up one success with the fourteen-day flight of Gemini 7, and Edwin 'Buzz' Aldrin, making his first venture into space. Aldrin possessed a powerful intellect and a zeal to match. Known to the Gemini community as 'Dr Rendezvous', he had written a doctoral thesis at Massachusetts Institute of Technology on the techniques of docking spaceships under human, rather than machine control. This was

Armstrong (right) and Scott at the end of a busted flight.

The launch of a Titan: multiple-exposure photography captures the moment of truth for Young and Collins.

'rendezvous by hand', and Aldrin pursued it with a passion equalled only by his determination to overcome the nemesis of spacewalking.

No sooner had they got to orbit than Aldrin was given a chance to prove the value of rendezvous by hand. Gemini 12's radar locked on to the Agena target, then lost it and crapped out. Without radar, Lovell and Aldrin had no mechanical means of determining the sets of equations that would get them to the target. Dr Rendezvous came into his own, pored over the set of space charts he'd constructed, and cranked the necessary corrections into the computer.

The course adjustments worked perfectly. There, in front of them, was the gleaming bulk of the Agena switch engine. It was another, this time unplanned, space first: Dr Rendezvous had again proved man's usefulness in space.

Lovell and Aldrin missed the spectacular ride to altitude because of a fault in the Agena's main engine. There was no way NASA was going to risk stranding

'Ride 'em, cowboy.' Gordon straddles Gemini bareback.

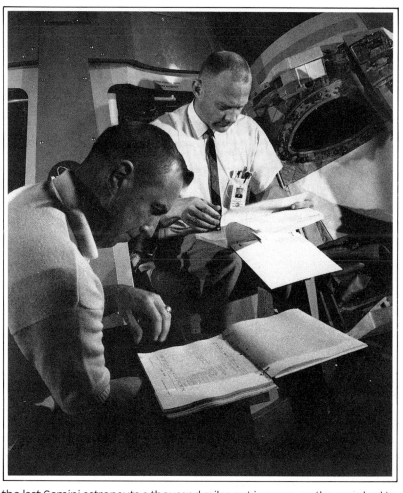

Dr Rendezvous (right) pores over his space charts as engineers prepare the final Gemini flight.

the last Gemini astronauts a thousand miles out in space, so the crew had to make do with a walk outside.

This was Aldrin's second chance to prove that astronauts could do more than sit passively back in a spaceship while computers and men on the ground did all the work. Spacewalking, with its opportunities to carry out inspections, repairs and even construction work outside the confines of a cramped capsule, seemed too exhausting for the human frame.

Spacemen from Leonov to Gordon had become tired, disoriented and panicky outside the safety of their ships. There was even talk of abandoning the whole idea: it seemed simply too dangerous.

Aldrin took the same attitude towards spacewalking as he had towards rendezvous in orbit. It **was** possible, all you had to do was to find the right approach. Long before his flight, he and some like-minded engineers worked out an entire battery of techniques underwater, in what was called a 'neutral bouyancy tank', which was basically a swimming pool kitted out with a variety of apparatus to simulate the environment of zero-g space.

Here Aldrin splashed about for days on end, until he was sure of the problems and the solutions. The former he identified as the lack of restraints — without any gravity to hold you down in the peculiar terrain of outer space you could well spend vital minutes flailing about wildly in search of something to hold onto — and the latter was to equip himself and the Gemini-Agena combo with as many straps, handrails, tethers, footrests and grippers as a bondage parlour.

As he drifted out of the open hatch, Aldrin's first problem was adjusting to the mind-numbing panorama of planet below him and stars above him. It was too much, even for a trained astronaut with a doctorate from MIT. He just drifted about marvelling in near-speechless awe at the entire universe spread out all around him.

After he'd recovered from such overwhelming cosmic culture-shock, Aldrin embarked on his quest to slay the spacewalk dragon. He clambered over Gemini-Agena with all the dexterity of Spiderman, then went to work on a spaceman's version of a kid's educational toy. He fastened and unfastened connectors, tightened and loosened bolts, played around with electrical fittings with little more difficulty than if he were a handyman back on earth. Everything worked, more or less, just like it should do: the restraints and handrails kept him in position, while special 'space slippers' and Velcro-studded gloves gave him some measure of purchase on the spacecraft. In all, Buzz Aldrin spent five-and-a-half hours out in space, more than anyone before him, and he returned to the spacecraft weary but fit. Dr Rendezvous had slain the dragon.

It seemed a fitting end to Gemini. From March 1965 to 15 November 1966, when Lovell and Aldrin dropped into the Atlantic, American astronauts had made ten flights, rendezvoused ten times with target ships, docked nine times and set a score of other space records. During that period, not one Russian had flown in space. Commentators started talking of 'throwing the space scorecard away', since America had obviously gained first place in the space race. President Johnson was prompted to declare that 'America is in space to stay', and Joe Public, faced with the regular and successful Gemini flights, forgot the humiliation of the Sputnik days and looked with pride and emotion upon the victory of America over her great space rival.

Ten for ten: Aldrin (left) and Lovell doff caps on carrier deck. Says President Johnson, 'America is in space to stay,' and it's the Americans' turn to crow.

CHAPTER FIVE

DEATH AND DISASTER

AFTER GEMINI, of course, it became an accepted fact that Americans could, should and would fly to the moon. No matter that some spoilsports — mainly radicals — cavilled over the ethics or even the necessity of spending billions of dollars to send a bunch of test-pilots and scientists on jaunts to the moon instead of on housing, education and health back on earth. The great NASA constituency of white middle-Americans fully supported the country's bid to be first on the moon and restore its battered image at home and abroad.

And so Americans entered 1967 convinced that the road to glory lay straight towards the moon. A scant four weeks later the country was given a grim reminder of just how much that journey might cost.

On 27 January, the crew of the first Apollo flight were about to undergo another in a seemingly endless series of checkouts of their craft, Apollo capsule number 204. They were not happy men.

The cone-shaped capsule and its attendant engine housing had been hauled to the top of the huge new Apollo pad at Cape Kennedy for a 'plugs out' test, which involved sealing the capsule off from the world around it, switching over to 204's internal power supply, and running crew and capsule through a battery of checks and routines.

Nothing went as planned. First the engine nozzle shattered, then during another test the heat shield split wide open, and finally the fuel lines ruptured and the spacecraft cooling system packed up.

For Gus Grissom, the crew commander, and his partners Ed White and Roger Chaffee, the entire process was a constant source of irritation.

Grissom was not a patient man at the best of times. A gruff, taciturn test pilot, he had survived the embarrassment of being the only astronaut to lose his spaceship when his Mercury capsule sank from under him and had later flown the first Gemini mission. Now he was scheduled to go down in history as the first man to make three space flights, and they couldn't even get the damn capsule right.

The situation was no less galling for Ed White, the first American spacewalker, a handsome West Point graduate who, unlike Grissom, preferred to cultivate a clean-cut John Glenn image rather than hang around bars, drive fast cars and subscribe to the fighter-jock philosophy of life in the fast lane. Much the same could be said of Chaffee, the rookie of the crew, who had made his name amongst the flying fraternity by taking U-2 spy planes over Cuba during the '62 missile crisis and who now had his sights fixed firmly on the moon landing.

They were three unhappy astronauts, and here they were, fully-suited and carrying portable oxygen packs, going up in the elevator to the 22-storey mark for yet another weary session in Apollo 204.

Up there in the 'white room', the sterile area where they would be checked out before clambering into the capsule, they met Wally Schirra, commander of the back-up crew. Schirra refused to stay around any longer than necessary and was on his way out. With a shake of his head, he advised his friend Grissom: 'If you have a problem. . . get out of the cabin until they've cleaned it up.' Then he was out the door.

The three men, helmeted and uncomfortable, took their places side by side while technicians closed the hatch. This was another source of irritation —

(top) The crew of Apollo 204. (left to right) White, Chaffee and Grissom undergo yet another test. Within hours, America would be given a harsh reminder of just how much the assault on the moon might cost.

(bottom) A NASA technician examines the charred 204 capsule where three men died.

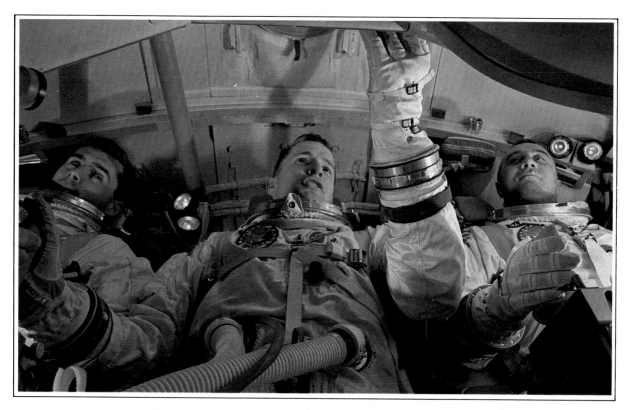

even with help on the outside, the Apollo hatch took over a minute to open.

It was the same old story. When static drowned out his radio link, Grissom blew his top:

'How the hell can we get to the moon,' he snapped, 'if we can't talk between two buildings?'

Then, at half past six in the evening, the technicians on the outside heard Chaffee yell 'Fire in the spacecraft!' followed by 'We're on fire. Get us out of here!'

The ground crew raced for the hatch. It was already red-hot, but no-one noticed in the mad scramble to winch the door open.

Neither did they notice the console readings behind them: White's heart-rate shooting up to critical; capsule temperature and pressure rising; the crew moving about inside the cabin. There was one sharp cry of pain, then silence.

By the time the hatch was open, all three men were dead from asphyxiation. It had taken just fourteen seconds to wipe out the crew of the first Apollo flight.

The following Tuesday, Gus Grissom and Roger Chaffee were buried at Arlington National Cemetery, the resting-place of John F. Kennedy, who had committed America to the goal of landing men on the moon and thereby the crew of Apollo 204 to their fate.

John Glenn and Wally Schirra stood stiffly to attention as rifle volleys split the cold winter air. Three jet fighters roared overhead in the 'fallen airman' formation, one wingman missing, as Lyndon Johnson read the eulogy for the two men who one day might have walked out on the moon. Ed White, spacewalker, was buried at his old military academy, West Point.

Meanwhile, the biggest internal investigation in NASA's history was underway. Hundreds of engineers and technicians were taken from their regular jobs at the Cape and assigned directly to a board of enquiry, as were the back-up crew for Grissom's flight, Walt Cunningham and Donn Eisele. Their commander, Schirra, remained at Houston where he took care of Grissom's personal affairs and raged at the stupidity of his friend's death.

Schirra's anger was shared by many in the world outside NASA and this time it wasn't just the radicals. Columnist Walter Lippman delivered a blistering broadside at the entire moon programme. 'We have had a sharp reminder that the race to the moon is not a spectator sport for which we only have to pay the bill and root for the home team,' he thundered, adding that beating the Russians to the moon was 'patently a quite unscientific attempt to feed our own ambition and pride and provide the crowds with a circus. . . We are risking the lives of the astronauts for national status-seeking, for pride, vainglory and tawdry competitiveness.'

Others questioned the wisdom of spending so much money — twenty-three billion dollars since the beginning of the decade on the manned space effort alone — to explore the heavens when the US was going through the biggest social unheaval since the war. Even Vice-President Hubert Humphrey got in on the act. 'We may go down in history as a people who could send a man to the moon, and five Coke vending machines along with him, but could not put man on his feet right here on earth.'

The entire NASA edifice, the big machine which employed nearly half-a-million people, stretched around the globe from the Cape to Australia, was in deep trouble, and the results of the enquiry into Apollo 204 only increased such feelings of introspection and doubt. Defective wiring which had caused a short-circuit to flash through the pure oxygen atmosphere of 204 was just one of many faults pinned down by the trouble shooters. The entire capsule, from the clumsy hatch down, was a tribute to bad design and careless workmanship. This was laid at the feet of North American Aircraft, the contractor, but NASA itself was also found guilty. Because there were no propellants aboard Apollo 204, no-one had bothered with fire, rescue or medical teams. In short, the crew had not stood a chance.

NASA had staked too much on beating the Russians to the moon and fulfilling the promise made by Kennedy five years earlier. The hubris of Gemini had led inexorably to the nemesis of Apollo. It was time to put away the patriotic flags and the fat cigars, for the honeymoon was over.

The Agency was in big trouble.

As the glamour began to wear off and America counted the cost of its romance with space, the rumour mill put it about that the Russians were about to pull off a new space coup. Despite the Apollo disaster, it was felt that the success of Project Gemini had relegated the Soviet Union to second place in the space race. The Americans had made ten spacewalks since Alexei Leonov's spectacular effort, but there had been no further move from the Russians. To regain credibility and again demonstrate the superiority of the Soviet socialist system, the Russians needed a new first.

A week from May Day, 1967, the news agency UPI wired from Moscow that the flight would come within two days, and would include the most spectacular Soviet space feat yet: an attempt to dock a pair of ships and transfer their crews.

The following morning, Moscow announced the launch of their first manned shot in two years. It was the first flight of a new ship — Soyuz 1 — and its pilot, Colonel Vladimir Komarov, was the first Russian to make a second journey into space. With three firsts already on the scorecard, the world waited expectantly for another demonstration of Soviet cosmic panache, a new heavenly challenge to coincide with the May Day celebrations.

Instead, there was silence from Moscow.

Then came the news: Komarov was dead.

According to the Russians, Soyuz 1 was on its sixteenth orbit when the mission controllers received signals that Komarov was in trouble. While they

Komarov in training. His flight notched up several firsts: first Russian flight in two years, first test of the new Soyuz spaceship. . . and first Russian space fatality. Russia, too, learns that the space race costs lives as well as roubles.

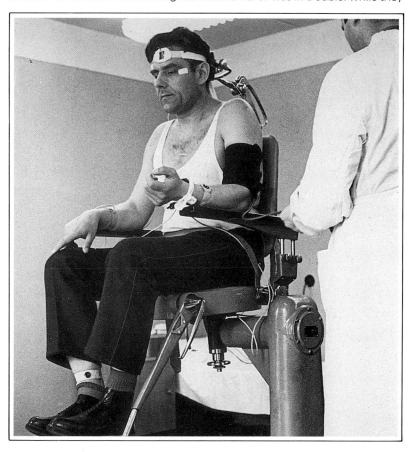

worked out an emergency return to earth, the cosmonaut made another two passes, lined the Soyuz up for re-entry, and fired his retros. Komarov made it back from the edge of space, but Soyuz' parachutes failed to open. Instead, they became entangled, and Colonel Vladimir Komarov hit the ground with the speed of a falling artillery shell.

There was no news of a second Soyuz launch.

It was Russia's turn to grieve for a fallen space hero. Komarov, an ex-fighter pilot, had been dropped from the space programme because of heart problems, yet had persevered and fought his way back in. As commander of Voskhod 1, he had proved his worth on that risky flight, and had been elected to fly the first Soyuz. He was slated for greater triumphs, had he lived.

One-hundred-and-fifty-thousand Russians filed silently past Komarov's bier as he lay in state. Then the funeral cortege, led by his fellow cosmonauts, marched to the sound of sombre music to a niche in the Kremlin Wall, where the remains of Vladimir Komarov were laid to rest near those of Sergei Korolev.

As the thunder of the cannons' last salute rolled across Red Square, a tearful Moscow woman echoed the feelings of those Americans who were wondering whether the race for space was worth the cost: 'Now maybe they'll slow down and spend the money here on the ground, where we really need it.'

Instead of a glorious new space triumph, the only scoop the Soviet Union could add to its list was that of the first death in flight. The fact that Komarov's death could be seen as the result of the Russians also pushing too hard too fast, gave American critics of the space race more ammunition. Even though Yuri Gagarin, in his eulogy to the dead cosmonaut, had promised that 'the Soviet Union will spare no effort to blaze new trails in space' it was reckoned across the water that the Soviet Union was well behind America in the race for the moon. Said **Newsweek** :

It should now be obvious that Soviet sights on space are set low... they are now lagging behind the US by a substantial margin in every category of manned spaceflight... There is no evidence that Russia contemplates a lunar landing program before the mid-1970s.

In that, **Newsweek** was wrong.

The Russians, like NASA, were now at a standstill: grounded by disaster. But there was no question that the Russians were in the space race to stay, and there was good evidence that they still had their sights set on the moon.

Only days before his death, Komarov told newsmen: 'I can positively state that the Soviet Union will not be beaten by the United States in the race for a human being to go to the moon.'

It was no idle boast.

Muscovites turn out to bury Komarov.

American military intelligence had known for months that Russia was running its own version of Project Apollo. The evidence was from USAF photo reconnaisance satellites, and it showed the construction of a vast launch complex some three miles away from the original Sputnik pad at Baikonur.

Marked by 600ft-tall observation towers, two huge concrete launch stands rose above the steppe. From the size of the service towers, the Air Force judged that the rockets they were built to handle would be around the size of a Saturn 5: over 300ft tall, well over twice the height of Korolev's R7 Vostok launcher. Further evidence was gleaned from the bulky assembly building which stood away from the pads and was linked to them by double sets of rail tracks. It would have covered two football pitches with room to spare.

Of the big rocket, Russia's 'superbooster', there was no sign. When NASA boss James Webb raised the possibility that the Soviet Union was developing a rocket as big as, if not bigger than the Saturn 5, Washington disbelievers dismissed it as just another NASA ploy to lever more bucks out of Congress. They labelled the mythical monster 'Webb's Giant' and chuckled derisively.

Despite the Apollo fire, by October '67 — the tenth anniversary of Sputnik — Americans had regained pride in their country's record in space. They could look to the moon, where a Surveyor spacecraft was checking out the lunar surface prior to Apollo; to deep space, where Mariner 5 raced a Soviet probe to the planet Venus; and to the skies above earth, where a fleet of weather satellites was busy sending back thousands of pictures of the planet's cloud patterns. As they phoned distant relatives via continent-spanning comsats or tuned into the latest live telecast bounced off the same craft loitering some 23,000 miles above the equator, they might muse on the ten years that had passed since the confidence-shattering autumn of 1957, and find no fault with the NASA spokesman who remarked 'I think it's fair to say that we are better than they are.'

'They', of course, were the Russians: the formidable commissars of the skies, now relegated to runners-up in the space race. But now the country was faced with other adversaries, from the armies of Communist North Vietnam to the 'enemy at home', the radicals, pot-smoking hippies and black rioters, to pollution, inflation and the thousand other maladies of a post-industrial society. The optimism of the Kennedy era was gone, the honeymoon in space was over, and it surprised no-one except NASA that public interest in the space race was on the wane and Congress was chopping away at the Agency's budget in order to finance the war in South-East Asia. Even then, they could look to the moon landing and hope, like *Time* magazine, that 'the feat will exert a great galvanic effect on the popular imagination. Those first reports back from the moon ("What a lovely earth out tonight!") may launch man into a bright new decade of scientific and human adventure.'

Unless, of course, the Russians got there first.

In the New Year, NASA sent the last of its Surveyor scout ships out to the moon. Between them, the Surveyor soft-landers and Lunar Orbiters had sent back a wealth of information on possible landing sites and the nature of the moon itself. There was now no doubt that the lunar surface was firm enough to support a man-carrying spaceship, despite some pessimists who were of the opinion that Apollo astronauts would sink, ship and all, into a cosmic quicksand, never to be seen again.

With only a year-and-a-half to go to the first planned Apollo landing, the Agency was pushing the moon race as a great Olympiad in the sky. At the same time it was keeping its collective fingers crossed that the Russians would not take advantage of that 18-month hiatus to pull off a massive pre-emptive lunar coup.

The first positive signal that the Soviet Union had its sights set on the moon came in the first weeks of 1968, when an unmanned ship was sent out into deep space. This was Zond 4, and its official mission, according to the Soviets, was to test new hardware 'in distant regions of circumterrestrial space'. Since

(left) Valentina Gagarin says goodbye to her husband. Only years later did the Russians reveal that Gagarin's body was never found.

(right) In happier days: Soviet space heroes Gagarin, Tereshkova and Leonov.

Zond 4 weighed nearly three times as much as previous craft in the series and was launched not by an R7 but the larger Proton booster, it was obvious that the Russians were up to something.

As America watched and waited for its rival's next move, the Soviet Union blasted two unmanned ships into earth orbit, then docked them by remote control. Both ships were Soyuz types, similar to the ill-fated Soyuz 1 which carried Vladimir Komarov to his death, and it looked as though the Russians were testing out the same technique — rendezvous in orbit — that NASA planned for Project Apollo.

Another clue to Soviet intentions came when two American astronauts met Pavel Belyayev, pilot of Voskhod 1, at the Paris Air Show. They found that Belyayev, too, expected to fly around the moon in the near future.

Before the awaited lunar triumph came tragedy. Yuri Gagarin, the first man in space and a heroic example of Soviet manhood, was killed in a jet crash just a few days after his 34th birthday. The news rocked Russia: first Komarov, now Gagarin. Again there was the slow procession to the Kremlin Wall, the eulogies and the mourning; made more poignant by the knowledge that Gagarin, after years spent as ambassador-at-large, was back in training for his second spaceflight.

And still the Soviets poured roubles and resources into the moon race, despite the disasters and the tragedies. They were also looking further than the moon, to a bright future of — according to the head of the Soviet Academy of Sciences — 'interplanetary stations and the reaching of other planets.'

By contrast, Project Apollo seemed like the end of the line for NASA. All across the country, the agency was laying off engineers and technicians by the thousand: on the very same day that the first Saturn 5 rocket made a successful test flight, 700 NASA employees picked up their final paycheck. Most of the flights to Mars and Venus had been scrapped or postponed, which led to accusations from space scientists that the US was 'abandoning the planets to Russia'.

As for the future, NASA had few plans beyond Apollo. There was talk of a space station built out of spare Apollo parts, and even a 'spaceplane' which would zip around the world and land like a conventional aircraft. Both these ideas were in the planning stages only: there was nothing for the space engineers to work towards except the moon landing. 'There is no question that things will be bleak in the 70s,' said one NASA official. 'The question is, how bleak?'

With pressure on the budget, low morale amongst the men in the trenches and the possibility that the Russians would snatch the prize plum of first to the moon right out of America's hands, NASA decided to push hard on Apollo. In the summer of '68, the agency announced that the second flight, Apollo 8, would orbit the moon. This was something of a gamble, since the Saturn 5 moon rocket was experiencing the same sort of problems that had dogged earlier boosters, but NASA knew that the Russians were within a few months of staging their own round-the-moon flight. As far as the engineers were concerned, the moon race was neck-and-neck.

No sooner had NASA released the news than James Webb handed in his resignation. The boss had had enough. On his way out, Webb loosed off some verbal buckshot in the direction of the budget-choppers: 'I think a good many people have tended to use the space programme as a whipping boy,' he complained, then directed a few blasts at US complacency. 'The Soviets will be flying more flights and developing a capability in space at a much more rapid rate than we will. . . We are going to be in second position for some time to come.'

As if to confirm Webb's dire predictions, on 15 September the Russians shot Zond 5 moonwards . The flight was unusually secretive, even by Soviet standards. Close-mouthed spokesmen refused to say anything more than admit to the launch, and it was left to Jodrell Bank observatory in England to tell the world what the Russians were up to.

Using a giant 250ft radio telescope, Jodrell Bank tracked Zond 5 as it hurtled off into space, then announced that the craft would loop the moon and return for a soft landing on earth. As Zond 5 flew across the lunar surface, an onboard tape recorder radioed back great bursts of data, and even the recorded voice of a Russian cosmonaut calling off instrument readings.

After hours of silence, Moscow radio made a dramatic announcement: Zond 5 had splashed down 'in a pre-set area of the Indian Ocean', its mission 'fully carried out'. The landing capsule was taken to Bombay on the deck of a Soviet cargo ship, where it was snapped by press photographers. The photos showed that the capsule was the same shape and size as the re-entry capsule of a manned Soyuz ship — which is exactly what Zond 5 was.

Since the superbooster was nowhere near ready for flight, the Russians had to rely on another Korolev legacy, the new Proton rocket. This was a scaled-up version of the old R7 workhorse, and it had just enough thrust to propel a stripped-down Soyuz spacecraft around the moon and back. So Soviet engineers took out the equipment section of a spare Soyuz to save weight; beefed up the heatshield to resist the scorching temperatures of a fast re-entry; boosted the radio transmitter to give a strong signal from half-a-million miles out and installed a heavy-duty refrigeration system so that the cosmonaut wouldn't fry.

They were left with a spaceship with just enough room for a single pilot and six days' worth of supplies and oxygen. This they re-named Zond, and with it they hoped to beat the Americans around the moon. They needed only one more test-flight, because although Zond 5 made a triumphant return to earth the g-forces of its re-entry would have crushed a human passenger to death. Any manned ship would have to fly a sophisticated trajectory through a narrow re-entry corridor, losing velocity by dipping in and out of the atmosphere like a stone across a pond. But, even though a further test was necessary, they were just one step away from the moon. And the Americans had not yet flown Apollo.

CHAPTER SIX

THE MOON AT CHRISTMAS

SAID ACTING NASA boss Thomas O. Paine, 'I still think the first man on the moon will be an American, but I wouldn't be surprised if the first circumlunar flight is by a Russian.'

And so, late in the autumn of 1968, the two countries were neck and neck in the moon race. On the morning of 11 October, half-a-million people lined the beaches and roads of Florida to watch America rejoin the space race. It was 21 months since the Apollo 204 fire: now three astronauts were waiting to fly the first Apollo spacecraft into orbit around the earth from the same launchpad. That Wally Schirra, Walt Cunningham and Donn Eisele might face the same fate was on everybody's minds, except for the three astronauts. All Walt Cunningham could think of before the liftoff was 'OK, Cunningham, whatever you do, don't screw up'.

For those who believed in them, there were enough bad omens to keep a soothsayer in business for a lifetime. It was the first operational flight of von Braun's new Saturn 1B, a 230ft-high brute containing over a million pounds of liquid oxygen and kerosene; it was the first manned flight for nearly two years; and the last man to ride a rocket into space, Vladimir Komarov, had not lived to tell the tale. One Florida newspaper ran a banner headline over the front page: 'Three Astronauts Ready To Face Challenge Three Others Died For.'

There was a lot resting on the flight — possibly the future of NASA as well as the crew of Apollo 7. Failure would mean the postponement of the next flight, tentatively scheduled to loop the moon at Christmas, and the golden opportunity the Russians had been waiting for to scoop the lunar pot. If the failure were fatal, the agency might as well pack up and go home. The new President, Richard M. Nixon, saw Project Apollo as throwing posthumous glory on to his rival, John F. Kennedy, and would have been only too happy to scratch Apollo and hand over the manned exploration of outer space to the generals. As Walt Cunningham saw it, Apollo 7 had to show that man and space could co-exist: 'The public had to be convinced that our missions were not circus stunts performed by soldiers of fortune with a collective death wish.'

The countdown reached zero, the eight mighty engines ignited, and out of the second fire on Pad 34 rose Apollo 7, like a twentieth-century phoenix. It was the most ambitious first flight ever undertaken. Alan Shepard's Mercury cannonball shot had taken him into space for a few minutes; the first Gemini crew went round for only three orbits; but here was Apollo 7 on course for eleven days in space.

For spacecraft commander Wally Schirra, it was also a personal first: he was the only man to fly each of America's three generatons of spaceships — an honour that would have fallen to his old friend Gus Grissom, had he lived. Schirra was a true space hero of the hard-drinking, fast-flying school, with a domineering personality and a temper to match. It was Schirra who had advised Gus Grissom to 'get the hell out of the capsule' and it was Schirra who, in front of a packed press audience, had announced 'We'll fly the spacecraft when we, the crew, think it is ready.'

It was thus inevitable that when Wally Schirra came down with a bad head cold, sparks would fly.

The three crewmen of Apollo 7 shared a cabin about the size of a large family car, in which they worked, ate, slept, and performed their natural functions. If one man belched, the others said 'excuse me'. In this cramped, claustrophobic environment, Schirra's cold took on monster proportions. He sneezed, he snuffled, he filled up the spacecraft with used tissues and, finally, he took to his couch and issued orders from the sickbed. As his crew kept slipping behind the packed schedule, Schirra took it all out on Mission Control, roaring and bellowing from the edge of space like a cosmic Captain Bligh.

On the second day, they were scheduled to make the first of a series of 'live from outer space' telecasts. This was too much for the wrathful spacecraft commander:

'I tell you,' he snapped at the startled controllers down below,' this in-flight TV will be delayed without discussion!' He railed, he ranted, and he pinned their ears back, especially over the 'Larry Lightbulb' science experiments: 'I wish you would find out the idiot's name who thought up this test. I want to talk to him personally when I get back down.'

Then he delivered his edict and refused to accept 'any new games or do some crazy test we never heard of before.' The laboratory rats had rebelled.

When the controversial telecasts were sorted out, the daily TV transmission became the highlight of the voyage for the crew as well as for the folks back home, who dubbed it 'The Wally, Walt and Donn Show'. They began with a sign which read 'Hello from the lovely Apollo Room, high atop everything,' then performed acrobatics or shot a travelogue, with running commentary, out of the spacecraft window. All agreed the best show had the crew appearing upside down on the home screens.

For the viewers, it was a chance to see life in space, for NASA, the Apollo 7 shows perfected the world-wide TV system which would send 'live from the moon' telecasts into every living room, and for the astronauts it was a welcome break in the routine. They even won an Emmy award. 'The ham in us didn't just surface,' commented Walt Cunningham, 'we damn near brought back vaudeville.'

The shows apart, Apollo 7 and its crew settled in to the mundane realities of space travel. This was the first spaceship in which the crew slept not on their couches, but anchored instead by a cocoon-like 'sleeping restraint'. It took three days to overcome the falling sensation of zero-g, which Cunningham likened to a dream of falling out of bed, or falling interminably through space: 'Just prior to dozing off, our subconscious would signal the falling sensation and we would be fully awake with arms flailing.'

By the fourth day, the romance was over.

'We had grown accustomed to some of the most spectacular sights in the

The irrepressible Schirra aboard Apollo 7. Six months later, the former Mercury hero hands in his resignation with the words, 'I don't want to stick around as a half-astronaut.'

'Hello from the lovely Apollo Room, high atop everything . . .' Eisele (left) and Schirra during telecast.

universe,' mused Cunningham. 'Our world had contracted to the spacecraft and the mission.'

During their more philosophical moments, the crew discussed the subjective effects of spaceflight. Walt Cunningham, one of the few civilian astronauts, was fascinated by the visual and psychological paradoxes of their tiny world. Relative to an observer on earth, Apollo 7 was inverted. Were they then flying upside-down over earth or diving down *under* the planet while flying upright?

Some NASA psychologists had hypothesised that man was subconsciously attached to an earthbound frame of reference. Would astronauts feel a sense of loss, cosmic melancholy? This was known as 'the break-off phenomenon', a more sophisticated version of the old 'will they come back screaming mad?' question, and the Apollo 7 crew were not fooled by it: 'This one was so far out,' said Cunningham, 'that we had trouble even identifying with it.' He concluded that man existed in a self-centred frame of reference, rather than one tied to earth.

A more practical question for the crew to muse over was that of space-sickness, whereby astronauts suffered bouts of painful and depressing projectile vomiting for the first hours of spaceflight. Why were some prone to throwing up while others appeared immune? This was a problem neither the Apollo 7 crew nor the medics down below could solve.

A more prosaic, but solvable, problem concerned the most popular question astronauts were faced with from a curious public. Sanitary arrangements for space travellers had improved since Alan Shepard wet himself on the launchpad, although it was still no simple process to take a leak. A modified condom was attached to the astronauts and linked, through a system of valves, to a storage bag which was filled and then dumped overboard via an airlock. For the man in a hurry, it was possible to urinate straight though the system — albeit, as Walt Cunningham pointed out, with caution: 'With a perfect vacuum at one end of the hose and an essential part of one's anatomy on the other, we tended to be a mite careful in manipulating the valves.'

It was the 'solid waste management problem' (NASA's term) which caused the astronauts most dread. Before Apollo, most spaceflights lasted less than four days, so with a low-residue diet and the right sort of pills the entire process could be avoided until the hero returned from his voyage. On longer flights, it was tedious, messy and often shattering to the astronaut's nerves. It was fatal to be caught short. The complicated procedure, which took up many pages in the NASA manuals, occupied at least 45 minutes and involved paper towels, cloths, chemicals and a plastic bag. There was much manoeuvring around, and much unpleasantness.

Since the war in Vietnam was a hot election issue, the crew were forbidden to take any pictures over Hanoi. From their vantage point on the edge of space, there was little sign of human occupancy on the planet, let alone any evidence that Americans and Vietnamese were slaughtering each other in the jungles of South East Asia. Light relief from the problems of the world came when the daily news bulletin from Mission Control announced that John F. Kennedy's widow, Jackie, was betrothed to Aristotle Onassis. Responded Schirra, 'Beware of Greeks bearing gifts.'

Eleven days after they had left the Cape, the crew prepared for the return to earth. First Schirra cut the living section or Command Module away from the equipment section, then flipped Apollo 7 blunt-end forward.

Before dawn on 22 October, 1968, the three astronauts made their last pass 76 miles over Houston; a small speeding dot of light in the morning darkness. Schirra, watching through a window, exclaimed 'We're flying a pink cloud!'

Now Walt Cunningham did feel melancholic, at leaving space, not earth: 'Something I had gloried in and had truly loved was being taken away. The voyage was already assuming that dreamlike quality of a moment long ago in another place, as though I was remembering scenes from an old movie.'

After the success of Apollo 7, the road to the moon lay straight ahead. All it needed was for NASA to give the OK to a circumlunar flight. While America waited for the signal, the Soviet Union launched Georgi Beregovoi into earth orbit aboard Soyuz 3, the first flight since Komarov's fatal journey. Was this the prelude to Russia's assault on the moon? Would Beregovoi dock with another manned Soyez or notch up some new Soviet spectacular? NASA held its breath.

Russian TV viewers saw Beregovoi flash a 'V-for-victory' sign from space, but there was little for the Soviet engineers to celebrate. Instead of a great new extravaganza, Beregovoi merely manoeuvred around an unmanned spacecraft without even docking. An assault on the moon it wasn't.

The Russians contented themselves with cocking a minor snoot at the lively performance of Schirra and his crew. *Tass* praised Beregovoi for his 'self control' and mentioned that he had carried out his flight orders 'with pleasure'. The inference was, of course, that Soviet manhood never misbehaved, unlike the jokers and ranters at NASA.

As Soyuz 3 cruised over South East Asia, Beregovoi radioed greetings to the 'courageous Vietnamese people' and praised their 'heroic struggle against the American aggressors', then steered safely back through the atmosphere and made a perfect touchdown on the snowy steppes of Kazakhstan.

NASA breathed again. There had been no significant technical breakthrough, and no sign that the Russians held a trump card to upstage Apollo 8.

The relief was short-lived. Within two weeks, Tass announced the launch of another Zond, its mission 'to perfect the automatic functioning of a manned spaceship that will be sent to the moon'. Like its predecessors, Zond 6 was a stripped-down Soyuz, but instead of flashing back to earth on a trajectory so steep it would fry a human, the spacecraft looped the moon, then coasted back to earth and skipped in and out of the atmosphere before landing gently in Kazakhstan.

The lesson was obvious — the Russians had perfected an autopilot with enough sophistication to surf through the top of the stratosphere, shedding velocity and slowing the re-entry capsule as it did so. If Zond 6 had been manned, the pilot would have survived the fiery descent to earth.

Against all the odds, Russia was within striking distance of the moon, and there was still time to beat out Apollo 8 for the first circumlunar flight.

NASA now had no option but to commit Apollo 8 to a moon flight. The next available launch window, whereby a craft could reach the vicinity of the moon with the minimum use of fuel, was 20-21 December. For the Soviets, a launch window for Zond would open 9 December. The Russians could still get there first.

As America prepared for the first journey to the perilous wastes beyond earth's gravity, the news from Russia was not encouraging. Launch crews at Baikonur were working round the clock to ready a Proton booster and Zond spacecraft for their December window. Moscow rumours had already named the single pilot: Pavel Belyayev, Alexei Leonov's partner on the suspenseful Voskhod 2 spacewalk flight. A massive fleet of tracking ships had left Russian ports for stations around the world. The Soviet Union was poised, ready to take the honours for the first manned flight to the moon.

It was a nerve-wracking, nail-biting time for the Americans. There they were, within days of hurling three men towards the moon, and that great Olympiad in the sky could still fall to their rivals, flying a cannibalised ship crewed by a single lonely pilot. It seemed downright unfair that the greatest technological power on the planet could be cheated by the brute force, outdated hardware, and sheer bravado of Soviet Russia. The supreme mastery of men, systems, computers, spacecraft, rockets and science that was Project Apollo would lie forgotten, eclipsed by the bravery of one Russian, if he were successful. It was Khrushchev, Korolev and Sputnik all over again.

The ninth day of December came and went, and there was no news from Moscow. Slowly, the assembled tracking ships left their stations across the great oceans and headed back home. Belyayev was at the space centre at Baikonur, awaiting final approval for his attempt to fly round the moon, but the decision was never taken. The risks of sending a single pilot on a half-million-mile trip were too great. Illness, accident or equipment failure would have been catastrophic for a spaceman with no backup and a bare six days' worth of air and supplies. If Khrushchev were still Premier, he would have damned the risks and launched Belyayev, but the men in the Kremlin were cautious, unadventurous and too keenly aware of the loss of face that would be caused by another death in space.

So Pavel Belyayev lost his chance to become the first man to the moon, and to have his name writ large alongside Yuri Gagarin as one of the true space pioneers. His feat, if successful, would have been magnificent. Instead, he was faced with disappointment and tragedy. He never flew in space again, and died a year later, like his mentor Korolev, under the surgeon's knife, the victim of yet another botched operation. He was buried near Nikita Khrushchev in a cemetery far from the Kremlin Wall, and the Russian people soon forgot his name.

With the Russians apparently out of the running, the way was clear for Apollo 8's moonflight, which NASA — despite a barrage of protests from irate Fundamentalists — decided to launch just four days before Christmas.

This was the billion-dollar moondoggle, the most extravagant American space spectacular yet, and by far the most dangerous. A power or oxygen failure could leave the crew stranded in space without hope of rescue. A malfunction of the main engine might send them crashing into the moon or leave them endlessly circling around it: a dead crew orbiting a dead planet. These, of course, were additional ways of dying. There were always the dangers of launch and re-entry.

'We are pushing our luck,' said nuclear physicist Ralph Lapp, 'gambling that everything will work perfectly. NASA experts will assure you that they have thought through the risks and have planned for them. Well, they didn't in Apollo 204.' Even spacecraft commander Frank Borman seemed less than totally confident: 'We have got danger all along the way,' he told newsmen, adding 'We wouldn't go if we didn't think the mission was worth the risks.'

On 21 December, Borman, his Gemini 7 partner Jim Lovell, and William Anders prepared themselves for the first flight to the moon.

Beneath them stood 363 ft of gleaming white rocket shielded by a massive

Pavel Belyayev, the cosmonaut who could have been first man to the moon.

The billion-dollar moondoggle: the Apollo 8 rocket inches down the tracks.

launch tower. This was Saturn 5, the biggest and most powerful booster ever fired, the final testament to Wernher von Braun's imagination and skill. In its design, Saturn 5 resembled a Manhattan skyscraper: thirty-six storeys high and weighing in at nearly three thousand tons, the behemoth seemed to reflect the awesome technological self-confidence of sixties America.

The countdown reached zero, the ground shook, and up went the first men to the moon, riding a pillar of fire into the sky above Florida. Two and a half hours after launch, Frank Borman fired Saturn's third stage engine, ramming them out of earth orbit and on course for the lunar target. They were now the first travellers to leave the home planet.

On 23 December, Apollo 8 crossed the 'Great Divide', where lunar gravity takes over from that of earth. The spacecraft's speed, which had slowed to a mere two thousand miles an hour, picked up as it passed the gravity gradient.

There was not much the crew could do on the outbound journey except check out the spacecraft and watch the earth recede behind them. Apart from the regular conversations with Mission Control and the occasional telecast, Borman, Lovell and Anders were alone in space, out on the edge and far from home. 'The long ride out to the moon was, frankly, a bit of a drag,' said Anders later. For Frank Borman, it was an especially hard time: he came down with flu and suffered attacks of vomiting and diarrhoea. Perhaps the shrinks who talked of 'the break-off phenomena' had a point after all and man **was** psychologically attached to his home planet. Problems of cosmic melancholia not withstanding, the crew of Apollo 8 were approaching a very real break with earth: the position at which they would have to fire the spacecraft's engine to slow them into lunar orbit.

This was the point of no return. Once the engine fired, they were committed to circling the moon (or crashing onto it) until the time came to blast out and return to earth. It was all or bust.

Apollo 8 was rushing towards a great grey desolate landscape, 'A ruined world, a globe burnt out, a corpse upon the road of night' in the words of Sir Richard Burton. Only essential conversations with Mission Control were exchanged, and these were terse and tension-filled. Frank Borman's heart raced to 130 beats a minute.

Astronaut Gerry Carr, their link at Mission Control, gave Borman and his crew the final go-ahead, then reassured them: 'You are riding the best bird we can find.' They began to curve around the moon, towards the far side where they would be out of sight and out of contact for the vital manoeuvre. Only the crew would know if it had worked.

'One minute until LOS (loss of signal). All systems go. Roger,' called Carr. 'Safe journey, guys.'

'Thanks a lot, troops,' replied Anders. 'We'll see you on the other side.'

Then the telemetry signals faded from the screens at Houston, and they were on their own, a quarter of a million miles from home and behind the moon.

There was an agonising wait at Houston. The minutes ticked away. Then, forty-five minutes after the consoles had fallen silent, the first burst of radio signals came through the void. As screen after screen flashed back into life, wild cheering filled the control room.

It was Christmas Eve, and Borman, Lovell and Anders were in orbit, 70 miles above the moon: the first men to look down on another planet.'

120,000 miles from home and heading moonwards — Borman ends TV transmission with waveoff. Said crewmate Anders: 'The long ride out to the moon was, frankly, a bit of a drag.'

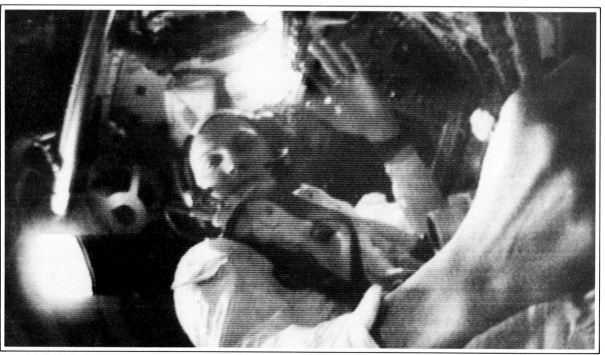

'The moon,' said Lovell in a casual tone of voice, 'is essentially grey. No colour. Looks like plaster of Paris. . .' According to Anders, 'the backside looks like a sandpile my kids have been playing in. . . It's all beat up, no definition, just a lot of bumps and holes.'

It had been a long, exhausting journey to a place far from home, so it was perhaps not surprising that the three men were less than lyrical in their reactions; that was to come after.

Late into Christmas Eve, while people relaxed around their Christmas trees, the crew of Apollo 8 set up the cameras for a guided tour of the moon. Frank Borman panned the camera down across the craters and dead seas drifting below, his voice crossing the quarter of a million miles to his earthbound audience:

'This is Apollo 8 coming to you live from the moon. . . The moon is a different thing to each of us. My own impression is that it's a vast, lonely expanse of nothing. . .'

'My thoughts are very similar,' agreed Lovell. 'The loneliness up here is awe-inspiring, and it makes you realise just what you have back there on earth. The earth from here is a grand ovation to the vastness of space.'

As Apollo sped towards the hidden face of the moon, Anders continued: 'The horizon is very, very stark. The sky is pitch-black. . . The contrast between the sky and the moon is a vivid dark line. The sky up here is rather forbidding . . . with no stars when we're flying over the moon in daylight.'

By now, the sun had dropped towards the horizon, etching craters and mountains in high relief. As they raced through darkness and into a new sunrise, the three men took turns in reading the first verses of Genesis to accompany the final TV views of the primeval wastes beneath them:

'We are now approaching lunar sunrise,' came Anders' soft voice across the void, 'and for all the people back on earth, the crew of Apollo 8 has a message that we would like to send to you.'

'In the beginning, God created the heaven and the earth, and the earth was without form, and void and darkness was upon the face of the deep.
'And God said "let there be light", and God saw that it was good'

Lovell, then Borman, read the final verses before the commander signed off: 'And from the crew of Apollo 8, we close with goodnight, good luck, a Merry Christmas and God bless all of you — all of you on the good earth.'

It was a poignant moment for the millions back home: there were the three wise men of Apollo 8, separated from their families and friends by a gulf so wide in space and time it was beyond the imagination, reading from the texts of Creation.

And then the pictures faded from their TV screens, the vital signs of spaceship and crewmen vanished off the Houston monitors, and Apollo 8 swept behind the moon.

Borman and his crew had hit the PR jackpot with the biggest emotional binge in the entire moon race. Everyone (save one militant atheist who sued NASA for equal time) was moved to tears, and for evermore in the hearts of the American people, the flight of Apollo 8 was 'the Christmas mission'. In fact, the Genesis reading was not as spontaneous as it appeared: the idea came from an official of the US Information Agency.

They were now two hours into Christmas Day, and it was time to fire the engine again for the return to earth. This was another moment of maximum danger: failure would leave them stranded in lunar orbit.

As Houston suffered a further bout of anxiety, the word came from Jim Lovell 37 minutes later, as Apollo 8 flashed out from behind the moon. 'Please be informed,' he said, 'that there is a Santa Claus.' They were on course for home.

Apollo 8's inbound flight was uneventful, apart from the awesome views of earth as the planet grew larger. From 207,000 miles out, Lovell acted as guide

Earthrise from above the moon. Said astronaut Lovell: 'It was just another body, really, about four times bigger than the moon. But it held all the hope and all the life and all the things that the crew of Apollo 8 knew and loved. It was the most beautiful thing there was to see in all the heavens.'

for another live TV tour, this time of the home world:

'What I keep imagining is that I am some lonely traveller from another planet. What would I think about the earth?'

From his vantage point, Lovell observed the delicate hues of oceans, landmasses and cloudscapes: 'For colours, waters are all sort of a royal blue. Clouds, of course, are bright white. The land areas are generally a brownish, sort of dark brownish to light brown in texture.' There was no indication that the planet was inhabited — no roads, cities or waterways. Earth looked untouched, virginal.

From then on in, it was housekeeping. The three men caught up on the sleep they missed and cleared the cockpit of litter and loose equipment. They had passed over the gravity gradient and were accelerating. Earth was calling them home.

Then they were ready to face the last great challenge: re-entry. Frank Borman dropped off the Service Module, yawed the cone-shaped Command Module blunt end forward, and hit the upper atmosphere at 24,600 mph. They made the critical re-entry path, that 'keyhole in the sky', and roller-coastered over the Northern Hemisphere. Finally, just before dawn, the pilot of a jetliner over the Pacific reported seeing a fiery contrail five miles wide and a hundred miles long. Apollo 8 was home.

They came back to a welcome not seen since John Glenn's return, complete with world tour, hero worship on a global scale and as many medals and honours as their shoulders would bear. The one that mattered most, however, was a congratulatory telegram signed by ten Russian cosmonauts, including Yuri Gagarin, Alexei Leonov and Pavel Belyayev, which praised the crew for their 'precision and courage'. The losers had saluted the winners.

Not everyone was wildly enthusiastic about the flight of Apollo 8, or even that Americans had finally beaten Russians to the moon. Said Linus Pauling, Nobel Laureate and peace campaigner, 'Something is wrong with our system of values when we plan to spend billions of dollars for national prestige.'

Commented *Time* magazine: 'It is possible to look at the moon flight and shudder at the vast, impersonal, computerised army of interchangeable technicians who brought it about. . .'

Indeed, compared to the harsh realities of life on earth —Vietnam, student riots throughout Europe, the Russian invasion of Czechoslovakia — Borman, Lovell and Anders' journey to the moon seemed irrelevant. But even the most blasé could not dismiss the new views of earth that the three men brought back with them, or their descriptions of how it felt to be there, on the outer limits.

'It doesn't take much to see the earth out there,' said Lovell, 'all by itself — the only colour in the universe — and realise what we left behind.'

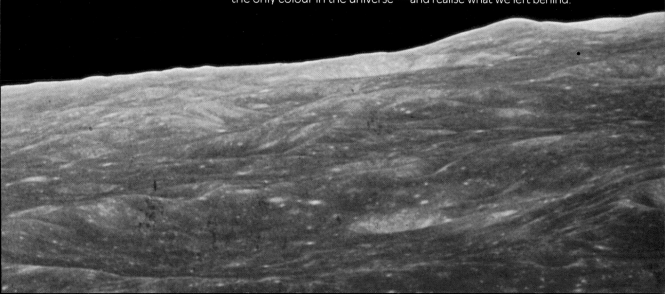

CHAPTER SEVEN

ONE SMALL STEP

TWENTY-ONE months after the death of Vladimir Komarov, Russia once again took to the heavens. Two weeks into the New Year, while America was still celebrating the first flight to the moon, Vladimir Shatalov rode Soyuz 4 into earth orbit.

The next day, 155 miles above central Asia, Shatalov watched as a trail of smoke and fire rose slowly towards him from the steppes below. His visitors were arriving.

As the crew of Soyuz 5 held their ship steady, Shatalov picked them up on his radar and started manoeuvring towards them. Out of the darkness, Boris Volynov, Evgeny Khrunov and Alexei Yeliseyev saw a dazzling white craft, whose solar wings were outstretched so that it resembled a giant bird.

Shatalov cautiously nosed into Soyuz 5 and locked the two ships together. Astonished Moscow TV viewers heard a scream from the cosmonauts: 'We've been raped! We've been raped!' followed by cheers and laughter. (This display of wild unSocialist exuberance was censored from later telecasts.)

More was to follow. Khrunov and Yeliseyev pulled on spacesuits and helmets, then crawled from the central crew compartment into the forward

After a twenty-one month hiatus following the death of Komarov, Russia again takes to the heavens. Vladimir Shatalov at the 'moment of ignition'.

Yeliseyev (right) gives Khrunov a helping hand aboard Soyuz 5.

'Welcome to the heroic crews of spaceships Soyuz 4 and Soyuz 5.' Minutes later, the cosmonauts dive for cover as the bullets fly.

'orbital module', leaving Volynov behind them. Inside the ball-shaped cabin, the two spacemen reduced air pressure to a vacuum and cracked the outer hatch. One after the other, they floated out over Latin America and the Atlantic Ocean, inched along hand rails and entered the open hatch of Shatalov's ship.

Five hours later, Shatalov and his two cosmic hitchhikers flew back through the atmosphere and made a pinpoint landing within sight of the recovery helicopters. Volynov came back a day later.

It was a great stunt — the first docking between two manned ships and the first crew transfer — and it gave notice to America that the Russians were still in the space race. If cosmonauts could dock and transfer between ships, then the Soviet Union could assemble a moon ship in earth orbit or construct massive space complexes.

Said Shatalov: 'The future, of course, lies with orbital stations made up of several ships. There is no point in bringing such a station back to earth. Crews can be changed regularly.'

At home, the feat was hailed as a great triumph, a consolation for Apollo 8. The four heros, together with Premier Brezhnev and a complement of fellow cosmonauts, drove through Moscow streets lined with cheering crowds. As the motorcade entered the Kremlin, a young Red Army officer stepped out from the throng and emptied two pistols into the passing limousines, missing Brezhnev but showering Alexei Leonov and Valentina Tereschkova with broken glass.

The bands played on, the triumph continued, and the shaken cosmonauts concluded that space was in many ways safer than the good earth.

With the door wide open for the moon landing that was scheduled for the summer of 1969, NASA went into overdrive to prepare the next Apollo shots, hoping to capitalise on the propaganda victory of Apollo 8. The mood was now less 'beat the Russians' than 'how to survive', because the American space programme was facing a new domestic adversary: the administration of President Nixon.

'Tricky Dicky' rode into power as a result of Johnson's inability either to end the war in Vietnam or silence the voices of rebellion at home. Instead of the tough Texan who regarded space as part of the political pork barrel — giving his home State the plum of Mission Control with its five thousand jobs when it could quite easily have been built at Cape Kennedy — the Agency faced a President who had served under Ike and his policy of 'calm conservatism'.

Space had not even featured in the '68 election campaign. Nixon had merely drawled a few platitudes about 'national interest' and moved onto more popular issues.

It seemed a hideous irony to the space engineers that after beating the Russians to the moon they were faced with more budget cuts and layoffs than ever before. From astronauts on down, people were either resigning or looking around for other jobs with better security. There were only five more moon shots, and that was that, so for a young astronaut there was no guarantee of a flight assignment.

The US space programme was as much a victim of the money-eating war in Vietnam as urban renewal or health care, 'circling aimlessly,' according to *Time* magazine, 'in a faltering orbit, out of touch with Mission Control.'

Along with the new Administration came a new boss for NASA: Thomas O. Paine, stand-in for James Webb, now officially confirmed. Paine came in fighting. At his acceptance speech, in front of an audience including the new President, he made it clear that he considered obituaries for NASA premature and launched an opening salvo: 'This country should indeed be the pre-eminent nation on space-faring and . . .' nodding towards Nixon' . . . with your help, Mr President, I am sure that we can go ahead.'

Paine then unveiled his plans for the American conquest of space : a further series of moon landings and scientific expeditions to that inhospitable planet;

a giant earth-orbiting space station; and the development of a manned rocket plane to ferry astronauts and supplies to and from space, just like the X-15 engineers had proposed a decade before. With all these 'blue sky' ideas bouncing around in the new enthusiasm for space travel after Apollo 8, hope was rekindled in the breasts of astronauts and engineers.

Meanwhile, there were two Apollos to launch before the final assault on the great Olympiad in the Sky, the moon landing. Apollo 9 was assigned the task of flying the most important, and so far untested pieces of lunar hardware: the LEM, or Lunar Excursion Module in NASAspeak, which would carry two astronauts from lunar orbit to the surface and back again.

The LEM was as cumbersome as its name, a flying bedstead of a spacecraft with four landing pads, a crew cabin which resembled the head of some giant sci-fi insect, and two separate rocket stages for landing and liftoff. It was functional, ugly, and had given several designers and engineers nervous breakdowns during its long and difficult gestation. But at last it was ready, and two Gemini veterans — Jim McDivitt and David Scott — plus civilian scientist Rusty Schweickart, were about to fly it around the earth.

This would be the first time any crew, American or Russian, had flown a spacecraft without a heatshield — since the LEM, nicknamed 'Spider', was designed solely as a lunar ferry in partial gravity and no atmosphere, a heatshield was irrelevant — so if anything went wrong, Scott in the Command Module, dubbed 'Gumdrop', would be called upon to make the first single-handed rendezvous and space rescue. If Scott were to fail, McDivitt and Schweickart would be stranded aboard Spider with no way home.

For the second time, a mighty Saturn 5 shook the skies of Florida, en route to the heavens. The three astronauts — known as 'the Rah-Rah Boys' since they were young, handsome and enthusiastic — rocketed into orbit atop the Saturn third stage. Once in orbit, Scott hit Gumdrop's thrusters and pulled away from Spider, which was stowed, legs folded, within a shroud forward of the spent stage. The Rah-Rah Boys then turned Gumdrop through 180

Gumdrop from Spider: another success along the hard road to the moon.

'The Rah-Rah Boys' after flight. (left to right)
Schweickart, Scott, McDivitt.

degrees, facing back towards Spider. Scott again fired the thrusters, and they docked. So far, it was OK all the way.

After blowing the bolts that held Spider inside its shroud, Scott blasted the combination into a higher orbit. They were ready for business. While Scott stood by in Gumdrop, McDivitt and Schweickart inched through the narrow access tunnel into Spider, sealed the hatches, undocked from Scott and flew their flimsy craft through its paces. There was only one problem: Schweickart was as sick as a dog.

To the medics, space sickness seemed like a malevolent force which could take over an astronaut at whim. There was little warning: one moment an astronaut would be bright and perky, the next suffering from vomiting and spasms of such intensity they floored the toughest space traveller. Rusty Schweickart went through hell, 200 miles out in space, weightless and inside a cramped and scarcely bearable spacecraft cabin. Only determination and self-control enabled him to survive four days of total misery.

But the LEM checked out and, although Rusty Schweickart never flew in space again, Apollo 9 was chalked up as another success along the hard road to the moon.

In May of 1969 came the full dress-rehearsal for the moon landing. Apollo 10 was to reprise both Apollo 8's journey and 9's test of the full hardware, with the added bonus of a trip in the LEM to within ten miles of the lunar surface. Some hawks within NASA wanted to go all the way for a touchdown, but with the Russians absent from the moon race there was no reason to take unnecessary risks. If Apollo 10 checked out, the crew of 11 would scoop the jackpot: the first men on the moon.

'I'd be fooling if I said I wasn't disappointed at not making a landing,' said Gene Cernan, Apollo 10's lunar lander pilot, adding 'we have been fortunate to have flown before and we know how spectacuar and beautiful it is up there.'

It was the most experienced crew ever to take a ship into space. Between them, Gene Cernan, Tom Stafford and John Young had racked up five Gemini flights. Right from the moment of liftoff the mood was more 'The Wally, Walt and Donn Show' than the dignified musings of Apollo 8's pilots. During a telecast from the halfway mark, Young hung inverted beside Stafford while Cernan, the joker, pushed the deadpan Young up and down with one finger. They closed the show with a tape-recording of 'Fly Me To The Moon'.

There were good reasons to be cheerful. There was not one sniffle or nausea attack during the outbound voyage — they even ate their stodgy 'space food' with gusto. 'All three of us feel tremendous,' Stafford reported, his strong Oklahoma accent drawling back across the Great Divide. The only problem seemed to be a buildup of gas in the crew's drinking water, with predictable consequences for their digestive systems.

But for the 'conservatives' within NASA, the crew of Apollo 10 would have made the first moon landing. (left to right) Cernan, Young, Stafford.

En route to the moon, the three men coupled up LEM Snoopy to Command Module Charlie Brown. Apollo 10 coasted towards its target, picking up speed, until the clumsy combo whipped around the far side of the moon. When they came around again, they were in a perfect orbit.

'You can tell the world we have arrived,' drawled Stafford as the flight controllers in Houston cheered, waved flags, and broke out the cigars.

Stafford and Cernan crawled up to the nose of Charlie Brown, cracked open the hatch, and manoeuvred themselves into Snoopy's cabin. They were in a compartment about the size of the cab of an underground train, festooned with cables, air fans and ducting. Each man had a 'flight station', at which he stood, held in place by a harness. There was no room in which to sit down. Thin metal panelling shielded them from the ascent rocket engine and its tank of liquid fuel. The only view out was through two small portholes at head height. It was no place to have an attack of nerves.

TV viewers saw Snoopy slowly cut loose from Charlie Brown, leaving John Young riding shotgun 70 miles above the moon. As Tom Stafford began the rocket burns that would take them within ten miles of the lunar surface, the two ships again raced round the edge of the moon. The minutes ticked away. Then came John Young's voice: 'They are down there among the rocks, rambling about the boulders . . ' followed by Gene Cernan: 'I tell you we are *close*, babe. Censorinus (crater) had huge boulders all around the rim of it, falling on the inside and outside . . we are coming up on Boot Hill. . .'

Twice they passed across the moon at around the distance of a high-flying plane, and then it was time to head for home. Resisting the temptation to drop those few miles and make the first lunar landing, the history books and a court-martial, Stafford and Cernan jettisoned Snoopy's spent descent stage and prepared to light the rocket engine beneath their feet.

Suddenly, all hell broke loose. Snoopy flipped head-over-heels and took off like a bucking bronco.

'Son of a bitch!' screamed Cernan. 'What the hell happened?'

They were pin-wheeling around the sky, fighting to regain control of the berserk spaceship, while the TV viewers back home grabbed their chairs and waited for Snoopy to smash into the hard rock below.

In less than a minute, the entire megabuck assault on the moon looked likely to end in a cartwheel of fire. Stafford and Cernan would have become the first dead men on the moon. But Stafford finally brought Snoopy back under control, and Houston breathed again. The cause was a single switch set in the wrong position. It was just like driving with the brakes on.

Finally, eight hours and four orbits later, the two shaken spacemen came back up, locked on to John Young's radar and inched towards a perfect docking. 'Snoopy and Charlie Brown are hugging each other,' reported a relieved Stafford.

Back inside the Command Module, the crew of Apollo 10 were finally able to relax: 'The crew status,' quipped Cernan, 'is tired and happy and hungry and horny.'

Then Stafford took the mike and told how it felt to fly Snoopy:

I guess I've flown over a hundred different types of aircraft, and that was my third spacecraft, but of all of them I never heard anything as noisy as Snoopy. It was too much . . . If you want a simulation, let your kids get a big metal bowl on your head and beat on it with spoons. . . It sounded just like you've awakened inside a rainwater tub with somebody beating on it like a bongo drum.

On their 31st orbit, the second crew to the moon fired up Charlie Brown's engine and headed back home.

Came the word from Stafford, to ritual cheering from Mission Control: 'Roger, Houston, we are returning to earth. The burn was absolutely beautiful and we've got a fantastic view of the moon.'

Cernan chipped in: 'The real view is in here: it looks like three monkeys in a spring bed.'

Added Stafford: 'As far as seeing a man in the moon, we just didn't. The view outside is great, but inside we look like three scroungy characters.'

And with that they came home, next stop the South Pacific. En route, Charlie Brown received a message from Houston: 'Congratulations on doing what I've been trying to do for a long time — The Red Baron.'

When Stafford and his crew reached home, preparations were already under way for the flight of Apollo 11 and the final assault on the moon, set for the middle of July and well within John F. Kennedy's time limit of 'the end of the decade.'

If the door seemed wide open for America, it was firmly closed to the cosmonauts. Two weeks before 11's final countdown, Soviet engineers moved the first of the G-1 'superboosters' on to its pad at Baikonur.

The colossal rocket towered 300 ft above the toiling workers as they pumped thousands of tons of kerosene and liquid oxygen into its massive tanks. Then, their tasks over, the launch crew retired to the relative safety of underground bunkers and watched as the massive steel launch tower moved away from the primed G-1.

The mighty engines thundered, the great tapered rocket inched into the air, cleared its tower, and caught fire. Within seconds, a searing fireball of kerosene and LOX tore across the pad, destroying all before it. Along with the burning booster went Russian hopes of a moon landing.

The last opportunity of stealing some of Apollo 11's thunder came just three and a half days before Neil Armstrong and his crew were scheduled for takeoff. If the Soviet Union could return lunar soil samples to earth via an unmanned spacecraft before Apollo 11, then the Americans would be forced into an embarrassing justification of the entire $29 billion moon spectacular. After all, if a machine could do as well as an astronaut for a fraction of the money, why bother to send men up there? Of course, no robot would have the same propaganda value as a cosmonaut, but it was worth a try.

So Luna 15 was shot to the moon, went into lunar orbit, and was still sitting there on the morning of 16 July 1969.

That day dawned hot and humid at Cape Kennedy. Around the edges of a safety perimeter stood thousands of reporters and TV cameramen; behind them celebrities, diplomats, politicians and royalty occupied the hastily-

Camp City at the Cape. Some of the million-strong armada settling down to witness the greatest show on earth.

erected stands; while further out a vast mobile armada of campers, cars and motorcycles settled down for the show. Some of the sightseers had been there for days, jockeying for best place in a jungle of screaming kids, necking lovers and beer-soaked bluecollar workers from all over the United States. All of them, from heads of state to motel cleaners, had gathered together to witness the greatest show on earth: the launch of Apollo 11 towards the moon landing, that great Olympiad In The Sky.

Wreathed in vapour, the white spire of Saturn 5, direct descendant of Hitler's V2 rocket, stood out against the early morning sky. Wernher von Braun, Saturn's designer, ran a final checkout from the Cape firing room. Other members of the Peenemunde team who came to America under Project Paperclip waited patiently at the rocket plant at Huntsville, Alabama or manned consoles at the Cape. They had come a long way since the grim days of World War II. They could afford to wait a while longer.

At Mission Control, Houston, Christopher Columbus Kraft, flight operations director, orchestrated NASA's Big Machine: the 30 flight controllers at four rows of computer consoles; the chiefs of booster systems, retrofire, flight dynamics and guidance; the flight surgeons and CapCom; the flight director, planning and operations officers; the staff support rooms which funnelled information to the consoles; the representatives from all major rocket and spacecraft contractors; and the communications personnel who linked Houston with the outposts of the big machine — the three giant radio dishes in California, Spain and Australia; the comsats floating 23,000 miles over the equator; 17 communications stations around the world; four US Navy ships; eight USAF planes and an entire fleet of recovery ships and aircraft.

The three objects of this interest and reverence were breakfasting on steak, eggs and orange juice — the traditional astronauts' breakfast — prior to suiting up. Of all the candidates for 'first men on the moon', Armstrong, Aldrin and Collins were unlikely examples of All-American Astronaut Heroes; those clean-cut, square-jawed Buck Rogers-in-the-flesh media myths.

Neil Armstrong, destined through seniority (having joined the astronaut corps before his two companions) to be the first man on the moon, was probably the nearest of the three to the accepted public image. A civilian NASA pilot and X-15 veteran, Armstrong had boyish looks that belied his age and all a born test pilot's judgement and feel for hardware. Armstrong was quiet and unemotional, and when he spoke, he gave the impression that everything he said had been rehearsed beforehand. A lot of his buddies just couldn't make him out. He was also the least athletic of astronauts: a comrade said of him 'if he felt the urge to exercise he'd lie down until it went away.' Everything about Armstrong was low-key, yet he had parlayed the dramatic

A boy and his rocketplane — Neil Armstrong poses with X-15 in his test pilot days.

Suited-up and waiting for the off — Neil Armstrong, destined to become the first man to walk on another planet.

(far right) Tension shows in Buzz Aldrin's face. 'Theirs was to be the glory mission, and they played it low-key.'

emergency return of Gemini 8 into the Buck Rogers Grand Prize — the first moon landing.

Edwin 'Buzz' Aldrin was at the other end of the emotional spectrum from Armstrong. His dedication to the theories of docking in space had earned him the title 'Dr Rendezvous', and he would talk long into the night about orbital parameters, plane changes and velocity increments. Aldrin wore tweeds and smoked a pipe — not mannerisms normally associated with hard-drinking, hard-driving astros — and had a keen social awareness. On the morning after the assassination of Martin Luther King, Aldrin led a memorial parade through downtown Houston, which didn't endear him to the politically cautious NASA bosses.

Michael Collins, who would fly the Command Module while Armstrong and Aldrin went down to the moon, was so casual he struck some people as downright lazy. Pragmatic and extroverted, Collins was the second spacewalker on the crew.

Ever since NASA had made the decision, six months earlier, to assign the first landing to Apollo 11, the three men had lived with the knowledge that theirs was to be the glory mission, and they played it low-key.

Not so Richard M. Nixon. Even though the new President had inherited Apollo from his rivals Kennedy and Johnson, he was more eager to get in on the act. Aides announced that the President would talk to the astronauts live on the moon, then fly to the recovery carrier to glad-hand them on their triumphal return.

The liftoff and the journey moonwards were uneventful. All the memoranda, meetings, reviews, milestones, simulations, procedures,

'Contact light. OK, engine stop. . . Houston, Tranquillity Base here. The Eagle has landed.' Aldrin on the moon.

checklists and protocols had paid off. Each of the nine million pieces of hardware in Saturn/Apollo worked flawlessly.

And then it was time to go down to the moon, live in front of the largest TV audience ever assembled. All over the world, parents told their kids to shut up and watch: 'The men in that rocket ship are going to land on the moon.'

Armstrong and Aldrin manoeuvred their lunar lander, Eagle, away from Michael Collins in Columbia, and headed on down. They passed the 9.4 mile marker set by the Apollo 10 crew, going smoothly until, just two miles away from the Buck Rogers Grand Prize, a computer alarm flashed red. It was hearts in mouth at Houston. Abort the mission! A damp squib! Disaster and humiliation, live in front of a billion TV viewers!

For a few seconds, the fate of two men and the entire billion-dollar moondoggle rested with a flight controller back in Houston, a young engineer who identified the problem — Eagle's computer had overloaded — and suggested the solution: ignore the computer and talk Eagle down from Houston.

His plan worked. The flight controllers relaxed. Go for landing! And at five hundred feet, Neil Armstrong took over manual control, jinked Eagle around to avoid a boulder-strewn area, and made a perfect touchdown on the Sea of Tranquillity with just twenty seconds of fuel left.

It was mid-afternoon in Houston, 20 July 1969, when the engineers heard Neil Armstrong's voice coming back to them from the surface of the moon:

'Contact light. OK, engine stop. . .Houston, Tranquillity Base here. The Eagle has landed.'

'Roger, Tranquillity,' radioed back Houston. 'We copy you on the ground. You've got a bunch of guys about to turn blue. We're breathing again. Thanks a lot.'

The next two hours were the busiest of the flight. Since they were out of reach of Michael Collins in Columbia, the two astronauts had to ready Eagle for an immediate emergency return, or face the risk of being the first men to be stranded on another planet.

Armstrong and Aldrin, too excited to sleep, moved cautiously around the cramped lander. Then it was time to open the hatch, and face the last great unknown — the surface of the moon. The great romances of the past, of ruined cities or underground civilisations, had long since been dispelled, but no-one knew for sure whether the ground was firm enough to support an astronaut. It was possible, if unlikely, that Neil Armstrong would disappear into a lunar quicksand.

Armstrong cautiously backed down the ladder, hopped off the last rung, and there he was, standing on firm ground. 'That's one small step for a man. . . ah. . . one giant leap for Mankind.' The words, muffled by his helmet, echoed across a quarter of a million miles, into the control rooms at Kennedy and Houston, where they were greeted by a great eruption of cheering. America had won.

Not everyone was so wildly enthusiastic. The Rev. Ralph Abernathy led a deputation of black protesters to Kennedy: 'We are here to protest, and we are here to demonstrate. We are here to say that what we can do for space exploration we must do for starving poor people.' Outside Mission Control, demonstrators carried a bitter message: 'Good luck from the hungry children of Houston.'

Far away from the troubled earth, Buzz Aldrin joined Armstrong on the lunar surface. The two men were in an airless, barren wasteland; a planet at the end of time. Nothing moved. There was no haze: objects a hundred yards away were as crisp as the outline of the nearby lander. Under a sky as black as pitch, the full force of the sun shone across a pitted, boulder-strewn landscape, casting deep shadows.

'You could almost go out in your shirtsleeves and get a suntan,' said Aldrin. He kicked at the thin layer of dust which coated the ground. Curiously, every grain described a gentle parabola and landed the same distance from his foot.

His attention was soon distracted by an urgent message from his bladder. He was about to wet himself.

'Neil might have been the first man to step on the moon,' Aldrin said later, 'but I was the first to pee in his pants.'

Neil Armstrong was fascinated by the moon's horizon, which was as sharp as a pencil line. The curvature was much more pronounced than on earth and there was no way of telling whether an object was one or a hundred yards away — as if, Armstrong mused, he was swimming in the middle of the ocean.

High above them, and unknown to the astronauts, Luna 15 began descending out of orbit. The attempted soft-landing failed: Luna 15 smashed into the Sea of Crises, and with it went Russian hopes of stealing some of Apollo's glory.

Meanwhile, Armstrong and Aldrin were experiencing a failure of their own — the flag-raising ceremony. Try as they may, the two men just could not get Old Glory to fly straight (Congress had firmly rejected the U.N. flag) and had to be content with a drooping Stars and Stripes.

And then it was time for the Presidential phone call. Nixon was chomping at the bit, so eager to get into the act that one Houston engineer wisecracked 'The President is go for landing'. But now the stage belonged to Nixon.

A this point Dr Rendezvous had a nervous attack. His heartbeat rocketed at the prospect of talking to the President of the United States, and the honour was left to Neil Armstrong to take the call.

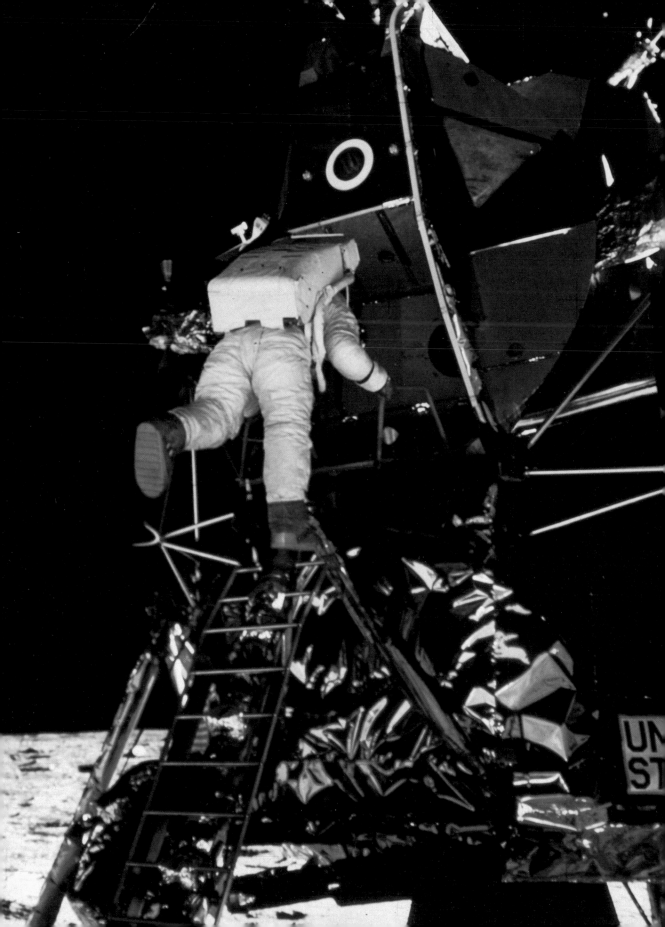

(right) 'Oh yes, we shall get to the moon, but of course I daren't tell Hitler.' Thirty years after Peenemunde, Wernher von Braun finally celebrates the realisation of his dream.

'Hello, Neil and Buzz,' crackled Nixon across the ether. 'I'm talking to you by telephone from the Oval Room at the White House, and this certainly has to be the most historic phonecall ever made... Because of what you have done, the heavens have become part of man's world...'

And Armstrong replied to Nixon's banal remarks with a platitude of his own: 'Thank you, Mr President. It's a great honour and privilege to be here.' Meanwhile, back on earth, a scientist screamed 'Stop wasting time with flags and Presidents — collect some rocks!'

Armstrong and Aldrin had a dozen experiments to perform — scooping rock samples and setting up equipment — and barely two hours left on the moon. So they bounced around in the moon's low gravity, explorers of the New World, with all the enthusiasm of kids on a school science outing. Then it was time to go home.

As they returned to Eagle and clambered up the ladder, Buzz Aldrin threw a small packet onto the ground. It contained medallions for Gagarin and Komarov, a crew patch for the Apollo 204 astronauts, and a small gold olive branch.

Inside the lander, they raised the cabin air pressure and doffed helmets. There was a peculiar tang to the air, a mixture of gunpowder and wet ashes. The moon had a smell.

As Armstrong lit the ascent engine and the two men blasted off to rejoin Columbia, Aldrin glanced out of his window, towards the moon. The Stars and Stripes had fallen over.

Back on the good earth, there was an epidemic of space fever. The **New York Times** used its largest headline ever, a Brazilian newspaper printed Armstrong's 'small step' speech in nine languages, others put large footprints on their front pages. There were 'moon parties' from Adelaide to Vienna. Scores of children were named 'Apollo' or 'Moon' and German police reported a sharp drop in crime while Eagle was on the moon. Pan Am and TWA accepted bookings for the first commercial flight to the moon — California Governor Ronald Reagan bought an early seat. In Eastern Europe, Luna 15 was ignored in favour of the Apollo crew. Said Radio Warsaw: 'Let them come back happily. Their defeat would be the defeat of all mankind,' and Russian President Podgorny wired congratulations to Nixon.

Others, with a natural immunity to space fever, dismissed the moon landing as 'a triumph of the straights', a mere technological divertisement, part of the bizarre social values of a society which could send men moonwards but not give its citizens a decent life. They pointed to the involvement of the same aerospace industry that created Saturn and Apollo in the Vietnam war, and to

(left) Faraway from the troubled earth, Buzz Aldrin hops down the ladder to join Armstrong on the surface of the moon.

'Neil might have been the first man to step on the moon, but I was the first to pee in his pants.' Armstrong snaps Aldrin.

a technology that seemed to be leading towards global suicide. Said an old Navajo Indian woman: 'I won't believe that the white man has got to the moon unless an Indian goes there and brings back the news.'

On 24 July 1969, those three white men, their names already entered in the history books, were floating upside-down in the Indian Ocean, fighting off seasickness and waiting for the arrival of the recovery teams.

They were plucked out of the water and placed in a big mobile home strapped to the deck of the carrier Hornet and sealed off from the outside world. This 'Mobile Quarantine Facility', was designed to protect the world from possible moonbugs. The astronauts regarded it as another Mickey Mouse stunt laid on by flight medics under the influence of too many bad science fiction movies.

Almost immediately, it was time for the Presidential welcome back to earth. 'President Nixon was clearly enthusiastic,' recalled Aldrin. 'He danced a kind of

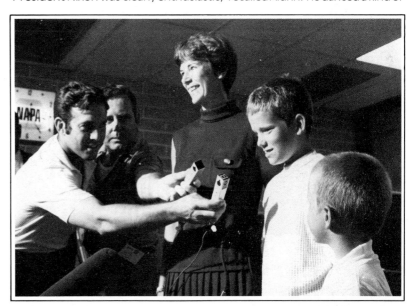

While the menfolk battled the perils of space, their families were left to deal with the Press. Here Armstrong's family puts on a brave front.

'President Nixon was clearly enthusiastic. He danced a kind of jig when he greeted us through the window and then went on to announce that our safe return concluded the greatest week since Creation.'

Adulation in New York. The three men of Apollo 11 drive through the city's largest tickertape welcome and a foretaste of things to come.

jig when he greeted us through the window and then went on to announce that our safe return concluded the greatest week since Creation.' Since the astronauts had no time to prepare any remarks, they were limited to a stream of 'Yes, sirs' and 'Thank you, sirs' in response to their Chief Executive's excitement.

After everyone had waved to everyone else through the mobile home's windows, Armstrong and his crew went through a series of medicals. There was no apparent deterioration in their condition. Their precious cargo of moonrocks — the raison d'être for the moon landing — was quickly flown under guard to Houston.

The men themselves took a little longer. After the Hornet docked at Honolulu, the mobile home was hoisted on to a flatbed truck and hauled to the nearest airbase through cheering crowds, where it was winched into a giant transport plane and flown to Houston, then on to another flatbed and driven inside a vast floodlit hangar to be greeted by several thousand people, including the Mayor of Houston and everyone who was anyone in Texas society, TV cameras, lights, reporters — and the astronauts' families. Their first conversation with their wives and children were conducted via telephone, surrounded by jostling reporters and popping flashbulbs. Armstrong, Aldrin and Collins were now public property.

Of the three men, Aldrin was the one to suffer most from 'post-lunar remorse', which he felt from his first day back on earth: 'That day on the USN Hornet was actually the start of the trip to the unknown. I had known what to expect on the unknown moon more than I did on the familiar earth.'

Their three weeks in the mobile home gave them some time to relax and prepare for their new roles as public relations men for the space programme. There was little to do except read, drink, play cards, watch movies and catch up on the paperwork. Aldrin filed his expense claim for the lunar journey: 'From Houston, Tex., to Cape Kennedy, Fla., to the moon, to the Pacific Ocean, to Hawaii and return to Houston Tex., via Government Aircraft, Government Spacecraft, USN Hornet, USAF Aircraft. Total expenses reimbursement: $33.31.'

On the twenty-second day, they were allowed home. Buzz Aldrin was amazed to find a gaggle of Italian paparazzi camped outside the front door. Neil Armstrong went out to sit by his pool and discovered three Japanese photographers climbing over his backyard fence. Michael Collins drove into town for a new suit and was chased all the way by reporters. The crew of Apollo 11 were back in the real world.

And then it was an endless round of triumphal motorcades, state banquets, foreign tours, glad-handing with Hollywood stars, royalty and billionaires; making speeches to adulatory audiences, medals, grand orders of, freedom of and keys to cities. The kings of space were reaping their glory.

Three years later, as a hospital patient undergoing treatment for a nervous breakdown, Buzz Aldrin, the second man to stand on the surface of another planet, found himself staring up at the full moon. 'You've been to the moon,' he told himself. 'You did it. First. It cannot be done again, not by you, not by anyone else. Now get the hell out of here and live the kind of life you want.'

Neil Armstrong handled the pressure for as long as it was diplomatic to do so, then retired to a quiet life as Professor of Engineering at the University of Cincinnati. Michael Collins announced before the flight to the moon that he would retire, and went to the Smithsonian in Washington as Director of the Air and Space Museum. Buzz Aldrin became a consultant to various companies, and a roving director for the National Association for Mental Health.

CHAPTER EIGHT

THE LAST MEN ON THE MOON

JUST THREE months after Eagle touched down on the moon, Soviet physicist Pyotr Kapitsa delivered a somewhat bellicose speech to reporters in Washington D.C.: 'We were well ahead of you in space, but you got to the moon first,' he conceded, then added with exaggerated emphasis: 'If you land two men on the moon, we will land three. If you land on Mars, we will land on Mars.'

The eminent scientist was bluffing — Russia had already accepted defeat in the race to the moon. When Apollo 8 circled the moon in December it signalled the end of Soviet attempts to send a single cosmonaut on a lonely lunar journey. Zond had failed, and the investment of billions of roubles and the efforts of thousands of Soviet space engineers was quietly written off. As far as the G-1 lunar landing project was concerned, whereby the giant booster would have launched a moonship to rendezvous with a manned Soyuz in earth orbit, time ran out when Armstrong stepped out on that inhospitable terrain.

And so the Russians, refusing to take second place to Project Apollo, turned away from lunar expeditions. Instead, they threw the resources of the Soviet space industry into a competition they were confident of winning: the construction of a manned space station in orbit around the earth.

A sight no cosmonaut ever saw — earth from deep space, snapped by an unmanned Zond. Russia had lost the race to the moon; now they were to embark on a new competition — the colonisation of earth orbit.

After the initial shock of losing the race to the moon had worn off, the Soviet information machine began extolling the virtues of colonising earth orbit. 'Man must build himself a house wherever he goes,' waxed one magazine, 'on the tundra, in the forests, in the mountains, on the bottom of the oceans, and now in space.'

More prosaically, a top spacecraft designer listed the benefits of such outposts: 'In the future, the volume of work conducted from space will increase. Crews will observe seasonal processes taking place on the earth's surface. Weightlessness and complete vacuums create ideal conditions for industrial production on big orbital stations. . .'

The anonymous designer omitted one other advantage of a manned space station: the ability it offered to observe and record military activity deep within an adversary's borders. Space was going to be the new high ground.

With the anniversary of the Russian Revolution approaching, it was obvious that the Soviet people were being primed for a new assault on the heavens. On 11 October 1969, Moscow TV dramatically interrupted its afternoon programme. Instead, viewers saw two smiling cosmonauts, clad in leather jackets and overalls, board a big Soyuz spaceship. Minutes later, cameras panned across the Baikonur space complex as Soyuz 6 roared heavenwards, heading for the biggest Soviet space spectacle since Alexei Leonov's spacewalk.

Within three days a second, then a third Soyuz raced up to join the two cosmonauts in Soyuz 6. The orbital troika manoeuvred to within a few hundred yards to form the world's first cosmic three-ring circus.

For five days the seven cosmonauts checked communications and navigation equipment in a trial run at orbital housekeeping. Soyuz 6 even carried a set of welding equipment, then regarded as a vital process in the construction of a permanent space base.

The message was not lost on the Americans: the skies again belonged to Russia, even though, in the words of a young Muscovite: 'It's not much compared with the moon, is it?' NASA was now suffering from post-lunar backlash. Having won the moon race, what could the Americans do for an

(left) Heading towards a 'cosmic troika' — Soyuz 6 rides the fire from Baikonur.

(right) The three cosmonauts of Soyuz 7 celebrate their successful return to earth.

encore? The space programme just wasn't selling. Congress, it appeared, was not interested in unlocking the secrets of the solar system, and promptly lopped three moon landings off the ten Richard Nixon had authorised. For once, scientists and astronauts complained in unison: the dumb fighter jocks because they could see their chances of going to the moon recede; the Larry Lightbulbs, for their part, wanted a bigger science return for the country's megabucks.

NASA launched a heavy PR campaign to sell the benefits of space, with everything from whistle-stop astronaut tours to articles extolling the merits of Teflon-coated saucepans and thermal underwear — both spinoffs from the space industry.

The blasé American public failed to respond, and when Apollo 12 set off on the second journey to the surface of the moon hardly anyone noticed or cared much. Once you'd seen one moon landing you'd seen 'em all.

Apollo 12 took off through a thunderstorm of such intensity only the Saturn 5's flaming tail was visible at five hundred feet. At a thousand feet, the big rocket was struck by lightning, knocking out Apollo's power system. Thirty seconds later, another bolt killed the computer. One more lightning strike and Pete Conrad, Al Bean and Dick Gordon would have been up amongst the angels.

They were already an unlucky crew — after the first Apollo flight in 1967, the timetable pointed to Apollo 12 as the first lunar landing mission. But as Project Apollo went off flawlessly, Wernher von Braun and the more adventurous of the NASA engineers pushed for Apollo 11, and Pete Conrad was denied the prize Neil Armstrong had claimed for himself.

Conrad was usually regarded by his fellows as having best bite at the lunar apple. Independent and outspoken, he raced sports cars and raised hell but always managed to play the NASA way. Dick Gordon, his fellow Gemini 11 pilot, was gregarious and cocky, while the third crewman, Al Bean, was a quiet, stubborn Texan on his first flight. They were a tight-knit crew with a heavy fighter-jock attitude: charge ahead all the way. And here they were, just minutes into the flight, in a badly-mauled spaceship, while Mission Control debated whether to abort Apollo 12 and bring them home.

For the first time, the engineers shed their ultra-cautious image and sided with the crew. On to the moon!

And so Pete Conrad and Al Bean rode their lunar lander, Intrepid, down towards that dead planet. 'I sure hope you got us lined up right,' drawled Conrad, 'cause there's sure a big mountain in front of us right now.'

The flight plan called for them to land within walking distance of Surveyor 3, an unmanned craft that had touched down two years earlier. This was about as easy as dropping a pea into a beer bottle from the top of the Statue of Liberty.

When the dust kicked up from Intrepid's engine settled, Pete Conrad suited up and stepped out — the third man on the moon. 'Man, that may have been a small one for Neil, but it's a long one for me,' he said as he dropped off the end of the ladder. Then he called back to Bean: 'Boy, you'll never believe it! Guess what I see sitting on the side of that crater? The old Surveyor. Does that look neat! It can't be any further than six hundred feet from here. How about that!'

Bean was already slithering down the ladder, eager to be out on the sun-bleached moonscape. 'Come over here! See that Surveyor sitting there?' 'There that thing is,' whistled Bean appreciatively. 'Look at that!'

They were two good ol' boys on the moon, chattering and joking as they collected rocks, peered into craters, and picked up more rocks. 'There's a good rock. Halt, halt, halt!' said Conrad. 'Look at that. Never saw one like that before.'

The two men bounced up the side of the crater where Surveyor had landed, peered around the dead spacecraft, then attacked it with bolt-cutters. Stashing their trophies in a backpack, Conrad and Bean continued with the main task: collecting moonrocks. 'Hustle boy, hustle,' urged Conrad. 'We've got a lot of work to do.'

Without the pressure of Presidents and public relations, Conrad and Bean were able to relax and enjoy the experience of low-gravity life on another planet. Even falling over was no problem — a one-handed pushup set them back on their feet.

After a day and a half on the moon, it was time to rejoin Dick Gordon. 'Man, is it filthy in here,' Conrad radioed from Intrepid. 'We must have twenty pounds of dirt and all kinds of junk. Al and I look like a couple of bituminous miners. But we're happy.'

'Liftoff and away we go!' he yelled as Intrepid's engine fired on cue. 'Man, this is a hot machine. What a nice ride.'

'Hey Pete,' radioed Gordon as the two ships drew together. 'How can you look so good when you look so ugly?'

And then the crew of Apollo 12 came home, racking up the second successful moon landing.

Two ships on the moon; Surveyor in the foreground, Intrepid on the horizon.

Meanwhile, the astronauts on the ground — including Alan Shepard — were hustling for a place on the five remaining Apollo flights. Shepard had been busting to get off the ground for years. After a serious ear problem kept him off the active list, America's first man in space took a desk job as chief of the Astronaut Office, made a fortune from outside business interests, and waited it out. Finally, Shepard's patience paid off. In 1969, he took a risk on surgery, emerged with a clean bill of health, and went after another chance at the Big Ride.

Shepard set his sights on the next Apollo flight, already promised to the only other active Mercury veteran, Gordon Cooper. The latter was generally regarded as an individualist with an anti-establishment streak. Shepard, on the other hand, was America's First Astronaut, a position which gave him considerable political clout with the NASA hierarchy. Astropolitics sealed Cooper's fate. The youngest Mercury astronaut was quietly taken off his moon flight, the crew of Apollo 14, led by Jim Lovell, were moved up a mission, and Alan Shepard went into training as commander of Apollo 14.

Having survived the change of assignment, Lovell's crew were in for another shock. Just a few days before they were due to leave for the moon, Command Module pilot Ken Mattingly was grounded after having been exposed to measles. He was replaced by Jack Swigert from 13's backup crew.

When Apollo 13 took off the world had already written it off as a foregone success. With two landings already in the bag, what could the crew of 13 do that hadn't been done before? One Italian newspaper headlined its coverage: 'Too perfect; the public is getting bored.'

The general tone of America's attitude towards the exploration of space was set during a NASA budgetary hearing: a member of Congress said he couldn't justify voting funds to find out whether there were microbes on Mars so long as he knew that there were rats in Harlem apartments.

Unlucky 13. In pre-flight pose (left to right) Lovell, Mattingly, Haise. Just a few days before the flight Mattingly dropped out. No-one could have predicted how vital his replacement, Swigert, would become.

So Jim Lovell and his crew headed out towards the Fra Mauro hills leaving yawns, not cheers, behind them. Lovell was another who bore the 'compleat astronaut' tag, even though he'd failed the Mercury selection board. This he more than made up for by flying Gemini 7 around the world for two whole weeks, then capped that by taking Apollo 8 around the moon. In between the marathon and the moon, Lovell filled time by flying the last Gemini ship. Now, with Apollo 13, he was the only man to fly four times and the holder of the all-time space endurance record. Said a contemporary of the 'compleat astronaut': 'If Jim fell in a creek, he'd come up with a trout in his pocket.'

This was to be Lovell's last flight; for his two companions, their first. Both Jack Swigert and Fred Haise were civilian pilots — Haise, like Armstrong, had flown for NASA before joining the astronaut fraternity. Swigert, the last-minute addition to 13's crew, was a former college football player with a reputation for having a girl in every airport.

And there they were, on the evening of 13 April, 1970, 206,000 miles out from earth, coasting towards the moon in the good ship Odyssey. Jim Lovell had just wound up a TV tour of the lunar lander, Aquarius, for the benefit of those back home while Swigert and Haise prepared to shut up house in Odyssey.

'Okay, Jim, it's been a real good TV show,' radioed Houston. 'We think we oughta conclude it from here. What do you think?'

'Roger. Sounds good,' replied Lovell from deep space. 'This is the crew of Apollo 13 wishing everybody there a nice evening and we're just about to close out our inspection of Aquarius and get back for a pleasant evening on Odyssey. Goodnight.'

A few minutes later, Houston sent up a request:

'Thirteen. We've got one more item for you. We'd like you to stir up your cryo (liquid oxygen) tanks.'

'Okay,' replied Swigert, 'Stand by.'

And then there was a crackle of static. When Swigert's voice came back, it was noticeably higher:

'Okay Houston, we've had a problem here.'

Queried Mission Control: 'Say again please?'

This time it was 13's commander, Lovell, who came on line: 'Houston, we've had a problem.'

Aboard Odyssey, the three men heard a loud explosion, then the ship started rocking and rolling violently. The master alarm sounded, lights flashed, meters showed both power and oxygen pressure dropped sharply. They were heading towards the moon and in real trouble.

Years of training and three days aboard Odyssey had honed the crew's sensitivities to a keen awareness of just how much their lives depended on oxygen, water, electricity and air pressure. Now, as they watched those vital signs ebbing away, they knew their lives rested on the ability to determine, within minutes, what had gone wrong — and to fix it.

Lovell, Haise and Swigert knew that something, maybe a meteorite, had ripped through the Service Module behind Odyssey, taking with it one of the two high-pressure oxygen tanks and two of the three fuel cells.

Swigert turned the two dead cells off, then threw switches to keep the third going. It didn't work for long. 'I don't have any current now,' he began to tell Houston, then added quickly, 'Hey, it's off! It's off. . .'

His voice trailed away. 'It's dead,' added Haise.

Peering out the window, Lovell could see vapour streaming by. 'We are venting something into space,' he radioed Houston. 'It's a gas of some sort.'

Neither Lovell nor Mission Control could bring themselves to admit, on air, that Lovell was watching Odyssey's precious reserves of oxygen leak away into the void.

In a desperate attempt to conserve enough oxygen to keep the crew alive, Houston directed Swigert to shut down the remaining tank, which was slowly leaking.

'Does it look like it's still going down?' queried Swigert.

'It's slowly going to zero,' replied Mission Control, 'and we are starting to think about the lunar module lifeboat.'

'Yes,' agreed Swigert calmly. 'That's what we're thinking about too.'

Just a few minutes before midnight on 13 April, out in deep space, Apollo 13 aborted. The third American moon landing had changed into the first extraterrestrial catastrophe, with the three astronauts facing a death no men before them had ever experienced: a slow cold death, alone and heading into the wastes of space. It was science fiction come terribly true. The crew were without oxygen and power and, since the dead fuel cells supplied them with water, that too. In just 91 minutes, calculated Houston, Odyssey would be completely dead.

The crew of Apollo 13 were not without hope, for they had two aces in the hole. The first was Aquarius, whose designers had built in an emergency life-support system for just this eventuality, and the second was Jack Swigert.

Swigert, whose presence on the doomed spaceship was solely due to a random measles bug, had helped develop the original emergency plans for Odyssey's manual. Apollo 13 was carrying the man who wrote the book.

So Lovell and Haise abandoned ship, drifting from a lifeless Odyssey, to the safety of Aquarius, leaving Swigert to close up behind them. One by one the lunar lifeboat's power and oxygen systems flickered into life. Their most important task was to transfer navigational co-ordinates — without which they were literally lost — from Odyssey to Aquarius' own inertial guidance system. While information went one way, oxygen went the other; through a hose cannibalised from Haise's spacesuit, to Swigert in the darkened command ship. Lovell and his crew could now fly the entire Apollo 13 complex from the lunar lifeboat, even to the extent of using Aquarius' descent engine to tow the dead Odyssey and its crippled service section back to earth.

Meanwhile, back on earth, TV and radio stations around the world were broadcasting newsflashes on the astronauts' fate, playing up the drama for all it was worth. At Mission Control and the Cape, hundreds of recalled engineers prepared to work round the clock to get the boys home.

One of the myriad problems both the men on the ground and the astronauts aboard Apollo 13 had to consider, fast, was a change of course. Unless the crew's trajectory was changed, they would whip round the moon, miss earth by thousands of miles, and eventually go into orbit around the home planet – by which time the crew would be long dead.

The simplest way back was to reverse course by firing the big engine behind Odyssey, in which case they'd be home in a day or two. Neither the astronauts nor Houston were willing to take a chance on that. If the engine or its fuel tanks were damaged, it would be the end of Apollo 13.

Alternatively, Lovell and his crew could use the smaller lander engine to slip Apollo 13 back into a 'free return' trajectory which would take them round the moon and back home. It would take three days – if the oxygen lasted out and nothing went wrong. Houston wanted to fire up Aquarius' engine behind the moon. Swigert disagreed: if they changed course before the moon, he could shut down the power-consuming control systems earlier, increasing their reserves. Swigert, the man who wrote the book, won the argument.

Five hours after the disaster, before dawn in faraway Houston, Lovell lit up the lander's engine. Thirty seconds later, the crew and Mission Control breathed again. They were on course for home.

'Okay, Houston,' drawled Lovell. 'Burn's complete. Now we have to talk about powering down.'

Half an hour later, with no reply, Lovell showed his edginess and fatigue: 'We don't want to bug you, but you ought to be thinking what the next burn will be. I've got to figure out watch schedules and the sleep schedules and how we can meet the next manoeuvre.'

They were tired, they were weary, they were far from home and they were scared. For the three men aboard Apollo 13, it was their longest night.

Inside the cold, dark spaceship, Lovell, Haise and Swigert took it in turns to snatch some sleep aboard Odyssey. One man was always on lonely watch at Aquarius' controls. This was *Lost In Space* for real.

While they slept fitfully, the engineers a quarter of a million miles away faced the moment of truth for NASA's big machine. Could they nurse the crippled spaceship home? Apollo 13 was still 74 hours away from the Indian Ocean – perhaps longer than Aquarius' emergency reserves could last out. There remained the grim possibility that the three men would die only hours away from home.

Houston decided to fire up Aquarius' engine one more time, cutting the flight home by eleven hours and changing the splashdown to the South

Mr Fixit in action, a quarter of a million miles from home. Swigert rigs emergency air system for the stranded astronauts.

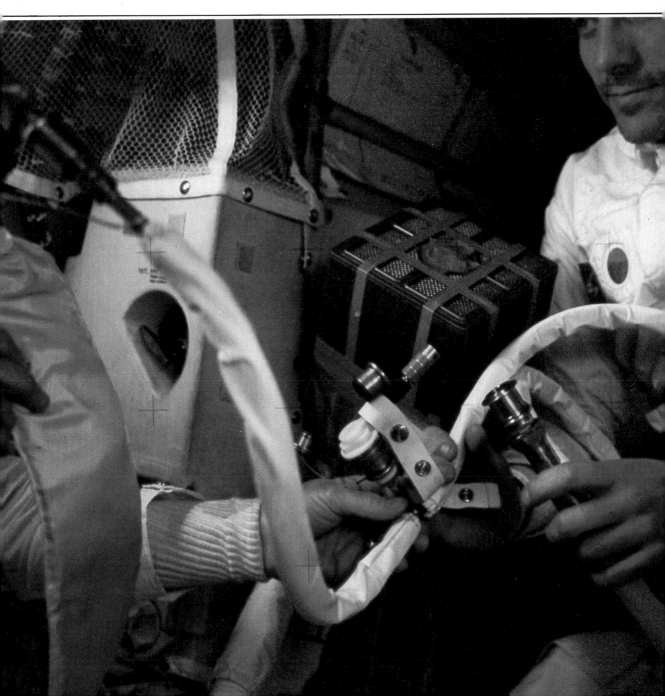

Pacific, where Hurricane Helen was causing havoc. Even the elements, it seemed, were stacked up against Apollo 13.

On the night of Tuesday, 14 April, Lovell and his crew reached the moon, though they never came closer than 158 miles. By the time they emerged from the far side, their glittering prize behind them, the crew were ready for the final 'hurry home' burn. So much debris surrounded the ship that they were unable to get a precise navigational fix from the stars: instead, Lovell improvised by taking sextant readings off the sun and moon. Then they fired up the lander's engine a second time and coasted towards earth.

After the crucial burn, Swigert powered every available system down to conserve their remaining resources. It was dark, silent and as cold as a hard winter's day, and they were faced with yet another problem. The lander's air conditioning plant, designed to handle the exhalations of two men, was breaking down under the load of three. The crew were in danger of being poisoned by their own breath.

Again they improvised, running a hose from the air purifiers inside Odyssey to the lunar lander, lashing it together with gaffer tape and stuffing socks in the connection to ensure a tight fit. Now they could breathe easily again.

During the long crossing back to earth, their tension and fatigue showed. The crew cursed Mission Control, garbled radio instructions and twice punched the wrong buttons. They were brought down — as much by the consequences of their busted flight as by their predicament.

'I'm afraid that this is going to be the last moon mission for a long time,' Lovell remarked to the others.

Back home, critics of the space programme were saying the same thing. Remembering the Apollo 204 disaster and the 18-month hiatus that followed, the engineers at NASA kept their fingers crossed and hoped that whatever caused the cryo tank explosion would not prove to be so serious that the remaining flights might be delayed or cancelled. If the three men died, of course, the chances were that Apollo 13 would be the last manned moon flight.

Meanwhile, the world watched and waited, tied into the drama by news reports on radio and TV. Even the Vietnam War took second place to the fate of the crewmen aboard Apollo 13. Said Pope Paul: 'We share the universal trepidation for the fate of these heroes.' The Russians, along with other nations, offered ships and planes to aid the recovery teams. And, of course, President Richard M. Nixon gave Apollo first priority: cancelling official business, postponing TV appearances and emoting concern.

Up above, the astronauts prepared for their last night in space. Each man

(left) 'Man, that's unbelievable,' gasps Haise, as the crew see, for the first time, the extent of their spaceship's damage. Replies Houston, 'If you can't take better care of the spacecraft, we might not give you another.'

(right) As the watching millions cheer, the crew of Apollo 13 make it home. Haise scrambles aboard life-raft to join Swigert. Lovell, captain to the last, stays with his ship.

wore two pairs of thermal underwear — Lovell pulled on his clumsy and unused moonwalking boots to keep warm while he took over the watch. Fred Haise slept in the docking tunnel between Odyssey and Aquarius, his head on the lander's engine cover. Jack Swigert crashed out on the floor, curled around the equipment racks. Fatigued and frozen, they catnapped while the spaceship sped on through the dark.

On the sixth and final day of Apollo 13's flight, the crew awoke so dozy that ground suggested they take two dexedrine pills each to keep them awake and alert. 'It's going to be an interesting day,' drawled Lovell.

Apollo 13 was coming in towards the re-entry keyhole. Said Swigert, as he inched into Odyssey's cockpit: 'That earth is whistling in like a high-speed train.' They were coming home.

The crew dropped off the crippled service module, then exclaimed with surprise as it slowly drifted off. One section had been ripped clean away, exposing wiring and debris. 'Man, that's unbelievable,' gasped Haise, aware of how near they had been to total disaster. 'It's really a mess,' radioed Lovell. 'Well, James,' replied Houston, 'if you can't take better care of the spacecraft, we might not give you another.'

Before they hit the atmosphere, Haise and Lovell joined Swigert in Odyssey, powered up for re-entry, and blasted away from their lunar lifeboat. As they watched Aquarius drop away towards a blazing death, Lovell paid his last respects: 'She was a good ship.'

An hour later, Odyssey skimmed across the top of the stratosphere. The astronauts steeled themselves for the last unknown. Had the heatshield been damaged in the explosion? Had they escaped a lonely death in space only to burn up within sight of home?

For six minutes, Odyssey screamed through the stratosphere, out of radio contact with Houston. Then, within sight of the recovery choppers and the TV cameras, the command module swung down gently beneath three orange-and-white parachutes. They were back, and they were alive.

The watching millions cried and cheered. Back in Houston, the flight controllers broke out the flags. In the contest of man against the perils of space, the soft machines had emerged victorious. The last word was left to President Nixon: 'There is no question in my mind that for me, personally, this is the most meaningful day I have ever experienced.' He then lit up a fat cigar and declared a national day of thanksgiving.

Neither Jim Lovell nor his crewmates ever flew in space again.

It was eight weeks before NASA released the results of an enquiry into the Apollo 13 explosion. It revealed an incredible sequence of bungling. Incorrect equipment had been installed in the ship's oxygen tank; the tank itself had been dropped during assembly; technicians had botched vital tests. The crew were sitting on a time-bomb. However, to their great relief, the engineers found nothing that would delay or cancel the Apollo programme. The moon flights would continue.

While NASA digested the news, their Soviet counterparts launched a two-man Soyuz into earth orbit. Vitali Sevastyanov and his partner Andrian Nikolayev, husband of the world's first spacewomen, spent 18 days aboard the world's most luxurious spaceship, with decor that included a sofa, table and sideboard – the latter finished in mahogany.

The Russians were serving notice that, having lost the race to the moon, they were not about to concede earth orbit to America. The new endurance record set by the two cosmonauts proved that man could survive weightlessness long enough to colonise a space station. The only concern for the Soviet space doctors was the physical cost – the crew's health deteriorated so rapidly that they had to be carried from their capsule. Space, it seemed, held terrors beyond those of mechanical disaster.

Neither were the Russians about to concede the moon to Apollo. If Luna 15 had failed to beat Armstrong and his crew back to the earth with the first

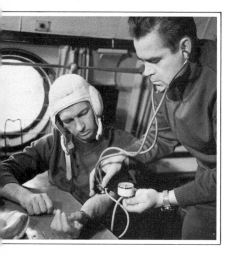

Alan Shepard (foreground) poses with his crew. Said the only Mercury astronaut to land on the moon: 'I was a rotten son of a bitch before I left. Now I'm just a son of a bitch.'

moonrocks, the follow-up was more successful. In the autumn of 1970, Luna 16 landed on the moon, scooped up a sample of lunar soil, and hightailed it home, landing less than 200 miles from the Baikonur launch site. It was an impressive technical feat, and the lesson was not lost on the Russian people.

'See, we're not so far behind the Americans!' crowed a Muscovite in the street. He might have added that Luna 16 cost peanuts compared with Project Apollo, and put no lives at risk.

Less than seven weeks after the lunar scooper, another spacecraft touched down on the Sea of Rains. This time, the ship disgorged a remote-controlled 'bathtub on wheels' – Lunakhod 1. It was the first giant step for robotkind. Operated by controllers back on earth, the ungainly machine, festooned with Soviet flags, pennants and even a bas-relief of Lenin, trundled around the moon for over 11 months.

Soviet engineers concluded a successful space year by sending Venera 7 through the caustic atmosphere of Venus for a touchdown on the surface of that inhospitable planet. It survived for 23 minutes, managing to deposit a picture of Lenin before expiring from a combination of heat (475°C) and pressure (90 times as high as that on earth).

And so the Russians, having lost the Great Olympiad, were staking a claim to the planets by robot proxy. NASA maintained that there was no substitute for a man's brain and senses, which had been proved by the successful return of Apollo 13. Conversely, the Soviets held that you don't send a man to do a robot's job. Cosmonauts were to stray no further than earth orbit.

When Apollo 14 set off moonwards in the early days of 1971, there was more riding on the outcome than on any other flight. Another disaster, and NASA could kiss the remaining flights goodbye. Said one engineer: 'If anything goes wrong this time, you'll hear the hounds baying at the moon – literally.'

For Apollo 14 commander Alan Shepard, who had hustled himself aboard at the last minute, failure would be more personal: 'I suppose if we don't make it back to earth, somebody will say the poor son of a bitch wasn't ready. But I am ready.'

Shepard, the first and, at 47, the oldest American to fly in space, took his crew off into the wild blue yonder, survived two near-disasters and achieved his ambition to land on the moon. At the end of a nine-hour moonwalk, Shepard produced a smuggled golf ball and whacked it across the airless wasteland. 'There it goes,' whooped the first man to play golf on the moon, 'miles and miles and miles.'

Not everyone appreciated Shepard's humour. Said Norman Mailer: 'Golf is insulting enough to people who live in ghettoes, but when we start doing it on the moon, there is something obscene in it.'

(far left) Nikolaev checks his partner's blood pressure before spending eighteen days inside the world's most luxurious spacecraft. They were less healthy on the return: both men had to be stretchered from the re-entry capsule. Space still held terrors beyond those of mechanical disaster alone.

(left) A bathtub on the moon. At the control centre for Lunakhod 1, engineers monitor Russia's answer to the Apollo astronauts as it trundles amongst the boulders.

(left) The steppes of Kazakhstan rock as Soyuz 11 roars heavenwards.

(right) The first men to live inside a space station: (left to right) Dobrovolski, Patsaev and Volkov before their flight.

Worse was to come. On their way back home, lander pilot Edgar Mitchell conducted a set of ESP experiments. The combination of golf and ESP was too much for some people, and accusing fingers were pointed at an agency willing to spend millions of dollars to send golfers and psychic weirdos moonwards. The astronauts just could not win. When they kept to the NASA-imposed public image, they were crew-cut machine men, taciturn and boring. Yet when they cut loose and revealed their humanity and sense of fun, they were 'insulting'.

If America's fascination with its astronaut heroes was fading, the Russian people were still looking towards the sky with glistening eyes. April marked the tenth anniversary of Yuri Gagarin's epic flight, and the occasion was cause for celebration – though tempered by the cosmonaut's death.

Celebrating that triumph of Soviet achievement, the steppes of Kazakhstan again echoed to the thunder of a rocket launch as a massive Proton booster lobbed the world's first space station into orbit. This was to be the Russian answer to Apollo: an outpost high above the clouds, where, in the words of Tass, men and women would observe 'the earth's atmosphere, life in its continents and oceans.' Like Apollo, space stations would be dramatic and risky, but of far greater value to science, medicine and industry. Space stations were the new wave, and Russia was riding its crest.

There were, of course, other benefits. To the military, a space station represented the 'high ground', a vantage point from which crews could observe troop movements, installations or even the wake left by nuclear submarines.

Science-fiction writers had long dreamed of space stations: floating cities where space travellers would embark on journeys to the planets. Richard M. Nixon had enthusiastically approved an American version, Skylab, scheduled for lauch in the election year of 1972.

In contrast to the romantic space cities of science fiction, where Pan-Am hostesses plied fatigued astronauts with coffee and muzak, Salyut 1 was built in Soviet Realist style: a collection of cylinders, resembling a fat telescope with two sets of solar panels which extended, fore and aft, like the wings of some cosmic insect. It was the size of a mobile home and weighted about 20 tons.

Salyut was followed by three cosmonauts in a Soyuz spaceship. The Soviet space engineers' euphoria was short-lived: Soyuz 10 docked successfully, but the cosmonauts left without entering their new home. The honour of

becoming the first men to board a space station went to the crew of Soyuz 11.

It was the Sputnik days all over again. Georgi Dobrovolsky, Vladislav Volkov and Viktor Patsayev cruised effortlessly into orbit, docked with the space station, cracked the hatch and floated inside Salyut 1. They were inside a chamber the size of a large living room, complete with toilet, kitchen area and even a small gymnasium. 'This place is amazing,' said Dobrovolsky breathlessly. 'There seems to be no end to it.'

Dobrovolsky and his crew became instant stars. Every night, viewers tuned into nightly telecasts that showed the cosmonauts joking and performing weird zero-g acrobatics. They enjoyed a freedom no spacemen before them had known: the ability to float, somersault and exploit the unrestricted volume of free space inside Salyut.

There were homely touches. At an impromptu party for Patsayev on his 38th birthday, the audience watched as his buddies toasted him with fruit juice. And there was the showbiz. Volkov, whose dark, rugged good looks resembled those of a film star more than a flight engineer, became an idol of Russian teenagers.

On 24 June, the crew passed the 18-day record of Soyuz 9 with no apparent physical deterioration. Soviet flight doctors attributed this to an exercise regime which mimicked life back home. Each cosmonaut spent four hours a day lifting weights (a trick made possible by springs attached to the bar-bells),

Volkov, idol of Russian youth, enjoys his zero-g training.

running on a treadmill, and generally working out. Even when they weren't pumping iron, the men wore rubberised suits that forced them to flex muscle or curl into a ball. Since the cumbersome attire caused the men to flap and waddle about the station, they were dubbed 'penguin suits'.

After three weeks in space, the excitement began to wear off. Dobrovolsky and his crew had set a new endurance record, operated the world's first space station and generally raised the morale of the Soviet space programme to a height not seen since Alexei Leonov's spacewalk. Now they were anxious to return home to their families.

'We have had enough,' Dobrovolsky wearily radioed mission control.

And so, after nearly 24 days and ten million miles – the longest journey ever made – they floated back into Soyuz 11 and powered up.

'This is Amber One,' reported the commander, using the crew's codename. 'Everything is in order. We feel excellent and we're ready for landing.'

Volkov took one last look at Salyut, their home in space. 'I see the station . . . it sparkles in the sun.'

'Goodbye Amber One,' crackled ground control. 'We'll soon meet you on your native earth.'

High over Africa, they began their long fall back through the stratosphere. After 20 minutes, Soyez 11 left the radio blackout zone and the flight

The crew of Soyuz 11 lie in state. Again, human failure and not space had been responsible for the deaths of brave men. 'The price they had to pay was not fair,' said poet Yevgeny Yevtushenko. Their ashes joined those of Komarov and Sergei Korolev.

controllers waited in anticipation for their first signals. Nothing came through but static. Then the recovery choppers sighted the bell-shaped re-entry capsule, swinging beneath its huge parachute. Retrorockets fired a few feet above the ground, churning up dust. There was still no word from the crew. The chopper crews raced over to Soyuz 11, cranked open the hatch, and peered inside. The cosmonauts were dead, hanging limply from their straps.

The news, announced on Moscow Radio, swept like a shock wave through Russia. Triumph had turned to tragedy. They wept in the streets and factories, hung wreaths around the cosmonauts' portraits, stood in silent, stunned groups around the nearest radio, waiting for more news.

All Russia ground to a halt. Westerners had seen nothing like it since America mourned the assassination of John F. Kennedy.

'This is such a terrible thing,' cried an old woman. 'They were human beings, they belonged on earth. Why did this have to happen?'

The embalmed bodies of the three cosmonauts, their open coffins covered in flowers, were placed inside the Central Army House, Moscow. Hundreds of thousands of men and women from all over Russia filed slowly past. A guard of honour, drawn from the cosmonaut cadre, stood beside the coffins. Party leader Brezhnev stood nearby, tears streaming down his face. Old women prayed openly — no-one seemed to notice or care.

The ashes of Georgi Dobrovolsky, 43, Vladislav Volkov and Viktor Patsayev, both in their thirties, all married with young children, were interred alongside Gagarin, Komarov and Korolev in the Kremlin Wall. 'The price they had to pay was not fair,' said the poet Yevgeny Yevtushenko.

The US astronaut corps sent messages of condolence to the men's families. Beyond their sorrow, the astronauts felt particularly dejected. Coming so soon after Apollo 13, the accident made the future of man in space look decidedly gloomy.

Had space killed Dobrovolsky and his crew? Was the stress of living beyond earth too high for man's fragile physique? 'Is there a limit that should not be overstepped?' asked a Soviet space physician. It was an important question, and it had to be answered, fast.

'In the ultimate philosophical sense,' argued an American space scientist, 'if it should be shown that space exploration is physiologically limited, then it means that mankind becomes the prisoner of his planet.'

Soviet engineers swiftly determined the cause of the second Soyuz fatality. Like the Apollo 204 fire, bad design, not the rigours of space, had killed the men. A faulty valve opened during re-entry, the rapid depressurisation caught the men unawares, and before they could complete the lengthy process of cranking the valve shut, they suffocated. Had they been wearing pressure suits, they would have survived – but the suits had been sacrificed to save weight.

That autumn, the deserted Salyut 1 space station tumbled out of orbit. It would be two years before cosmonauts again rode the fire into space.

If the Russians were dogged by catastrophe, NASA had its own problem. The signs were everywhere: boarded-up shops around Cape Kennedy; thousands of lay-offs in Southern California and other aerospace centres. The boomtown days were over. The money was running out.

When David Scott took Apollo 15 to the moon, hardly anyone noticed except Congress, which promptly lopped more money off the agency's budget. The future looked bleak for the astronauts: just two more moon missions and then Skylab, the US space station. There were more astronauts than flights.

If 1971 ended on a bum note, the new year brought the good news everyone at NASA hoped for. After years of proposals and counter-proposals, President Richard M. Nixon gave NASA the go-ahead for an ambitious new project that would assure the astronauts' future. Space Shuttle, said the President, would 'transform the space frontier of the 1970s into familiar territory easily accessible for human endeavour.'

The fact that NASA would be hiring thousands of workers during the summer, right at the peak of the Presidential election campaign, did much to encourage Nixon's enthusiasm for Shuttle, especially as his other project, Skylab, had been delayed well into 1973, denying the President an opportunity to point towards the space station as an example of the supremacy of the American capitalist system under its leader, Richard M. Nixon.

Shuttle would be the first true spaceship. It would take off like a rocket but land like an airliner. The idea itself was not new: the Peenemunde engineers had proposed such a craft back in the forties, and had gone so far as to test a winged V-2. Fortunately for the citizens of New York, its eventual target, the test ship's wings fell off and the project was abandoned. Other NASA variants included strapping an X-15 rocket plane on to a big booster and running that around the earth, or, in the case of the USAF, sending a small unpowered single-seater, dubbed DynaSoar, into orbit. Neither had made it for cost reasons: even the Shuttle was pruned down to the minimum. Engineers on von Braun's NASA team had proposed an entire family of spaceships and manned outposts, from bases on the moon and in earth orbit to space tugs. Shuttle, as its name suggested, was intended as a spaceplane which would carry men and materials up to earth orbit, merely a freighter in the grand scheme to conquer the solar system. Only the spaceplane survived, and that was pared to the bone. The plans called for both the spaceplane and its booster to be recovered, both craft landing like conventional airliners. Congress baulked at the $10 billion price tag, and NASA was left with only a reusable spaceplane. Even then, it was a close-run thing. Without the backing of the Air Force, who had lost their pet DynaSoar project but could see great potential in the spaceplane as a reconnaisance ship or satellite interceptor, Shuttle might never have been approved.

So there was relief within NASA. For the astronauts left over from Apollo, there was always the chance that, if they didn't die from old age in the interim, they could look forward to flying a true Buck Rogers spaceship.

In the meantime, there were just two Apollo flights to go. The penultimate flight, commanded by the ever-reliable John Young, now on his second trip moonwards, took off and was promptly forgotten by the fickle American public.

Meanwhile, President Nixon was hot-footing it across the Atlantic for a summit meeting with the Russians which, since it coincided with the height of the re-election campaign, was a political masterstroke. The new buzzword was 'detente'. No longer would the two adversaries threaten nuclear destruction. Instead, they would agree to cohabit the planet, growling but never biting.

To symbolise this new era, Nixon and Soviet Premier Kosygin put pen to paper and authorised a new space spectacular: the first rendezvous and docking between Russian and American spaceships. A handshake in space! The two great rivals in harmony above the planet! A fabulous metaphor for the new era!

Though thinly disguised as a test of a new docking mechanism for possible space rescue missions, no-one doubted that the main reason was political. Even Nixon's rivals conceded the magnificence of his stunt.

There were benefits for both sides. The US could use a spare Apollo ship, providing a gap-filler between Skylab and Shuttle; the Russians would gain access to US technology. If the new project were successful, then it might stir up new joint ventures in space. Said a NASA official, mindful of Congress' unwillingness to sign blank cheques: 'I would rather get to Mars with Russian help than not get there at all.'

So the Soviet Union, once again, breathed new life into the American space programme, even if this time it was through co-operation rather than competition.

That summer, Wernher von Braun announced his resignation from NASA. The man who had masterminded Hitler's V-2 war rockets, who had designed the Redstone boosters which launched both America's first satellite and spaceman in the grim postwar years, who had designed the giant Saturns that had placed Neil Armstrong on the moon, who had laboured on Shuttle and was, even now, building Skylab, the first US space station, was leaving the agency. With Russia and America talking of ending their competition in space, it seemed that an era was ending.

If the American public's enthusiasm for space travel was waning, so was the image of the astronauts. An internal NASA investigation revealed that, far from dedicating their lives to the national interest with no thought of personal gain, some astronauts had committed the mortal sin of cashing in on their position.

Along with the science experiments and the Stars and Stripes, the crew of Apollo 15 had landed bearing 600 first-day postal covers, most of them unauthorised, all of them signed by the astronauts. A hundred of these were later shipped to a German stamp dealer who sold them to collectors for $1500 apiece.

This was merely the tip of the iceberg. Wristwatches had been taken on the great journey for 'evaluation', thereby allowing their proud makers to advertise them as 'space proven', 'as used by the astronauts'; medals had been flown into space and sold for profit; even a sculpture, 'The Fallen Astronaut.'

This had been placed by the crew of Apollo 15 on lunar soil, along with a plaque bearing the names of the fourteen astronauts and cosmonauts who had died along the road to the stars. The sculptor swore blind there would be no commercial exploitation. Then lo and behold, copies started appearing at $750 apiece.

Oh, the scandal, oh the shame. There were Senate hearings and Justice Department investigations. Dave Scott and his Apollo 15 crewmates resigned or were shuttled sideways into desk jobs. They had broken the unofficial NASA rule and screwed the pooch. The supermen had feet of clay.

The petty nature of their transgression was out of all proportion to their fate. Most of the astronauts had at some time in their careers been propositioned by businessmen eager for their names on the company stationery, and most of them had turned the offers down. Stamps and medals, however, were regarded as legitimate perks, life insurance for their families should anything go wrong. In the profession of spaceflight, conventional life insurance was hard to come by.

Against the background of official hypocrisy towards men who risked their lives for the conquest of space and the national interest, NASA launched the last of the Apollo flights.

It was December of 1972, and the first ever night-time launch. Aboard was Jack Schmitt, the first scientist to head moonwards and, again for the first time, NASA threw a tight security order around the astronauts' families. The heady days of the sixties were past: Israeli athletes had been murdered at the Munich Olympics, and no-one was taking chances.

At midnight, Apollo 17 rode that great fire into the skies, cheered on by an ecstatic crowd. For the remaining astronauts, that night at the Cape was the last time they would be together to celebrate. Just 15 years after Sputnik 1 beeped its way across the skies and ushered in the space race, Gene Cernan and Jack Schmitt landed in the Taurus-Littrow Valley, near Camelot crater — named in tribute to John F. Kennedy, the President who had committed America to the moon landings and thereby erased the humiliation of Sputnik. 'Camelot' was his favourite movie.

Never before had the world seen such an expensive or inspiring project as Apollo, and even the Soviet Union was moved to express admiration: 'The last act of the Apollo epic has started, one of the most daring undertakings man had ever entered into. Three of the world's brave men are flying to the moon.

May success be theirs on this difficult road.

Cernan and Schmitt spent just over three days on the surface of the moon, then rejoined Ron Evans in lunar orbit. As they left, Cernan uttered the last words from the moon: 'Okay, let's get this mother out of here!'

The race to the moon was over. National pride had been restored.

It was the end of an era: of the astronaut as superhero, battling with the Russians for control of the heavens; as media star, the focus of ticker-tape adulation, the sought-after companion of celebrities and royalty. Never again would there be a Glenn or an Armstrong. Even the last men on the moon were nameless faces, soon to be forgotten.

Americans had grown accustomed to the spectacle and the drama: great white rockets cleaving the skies; spacesuited figures stumbling in slow motion across a barren moonscape; those last nerve-wracking minutes of re-entry and splashdown.

Before Vietnam, spaceflight had been glamorous and extravagant. Now it was only extravagant; a billion-dollar moondoggle which America could no longer afford.

(Inset) Saturn's mighty engines flame into life as Apollo 17 begins its long journey to the moon.

The last man on the moon — Schmitt examines boulder in the Valley of Taurus-Littrow.

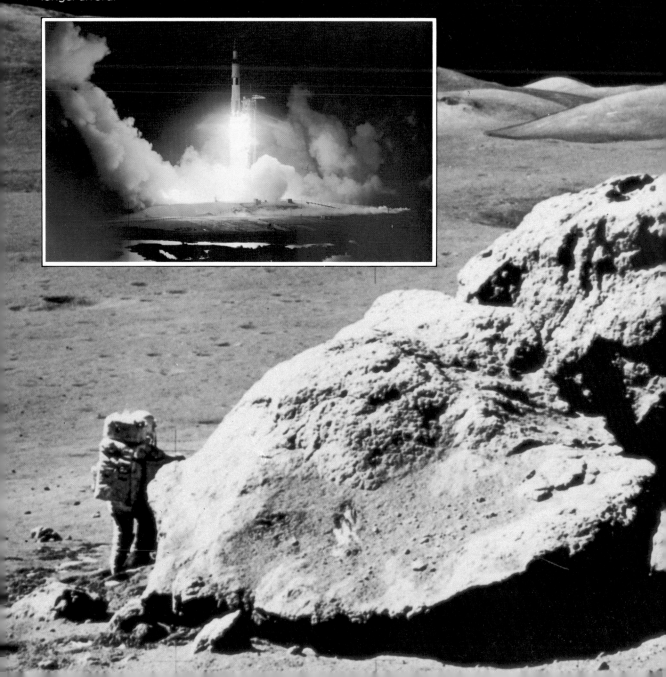

Project Apollo, the first great expedition to another planet, had run out of money. In the past, voyages of discovery had been patronised on the promise of riches from distant shores. There were no diamonds on the moon (nor '2001'-style monoliths) only rocks, a new vision of earth as a small blue planet in a vast black emptiness and, for some of its inhabitants, a new humility and awareness:

'I would like to tell you about a place I have seen,' said Jack Schmitt, the last man on the moon, 'the Valley of Taurus-Littrow. The Valley has been unchanged by being a name on a distant planet, while change has governed the men who named it. The Valley has been less altered by being explored than they who have been the explorers. The Valley has been less affected by all we have done than have been the millions who, for a moment, were aware of its towering walls, its visitors, and then its silence.'

3 COLONISTS ON THE EDGE OF SPACE

CHAPTER NINE

THE WAVE OF THE FUTURE

A S AMERICA entered the new year of 1973, NASA too was forced to accept the limits of man's ventures into the heavens. Gone were the great days of the sixties, when blank cheques fell like tickertape upon Houston and the Cape. Now Americans, like their cosmonaut rivals, would stray no further than earth orbit, because no-one could afford the megabucks to send them out into the dark reaches beyond.

So the future of Americans in space rested with Skylab, a second-hand space station making use of the spare Saturns and Apollos from the cancelled moon flights.

In April, even as the 5-storey-high space station inched down the tracks towards Pad 39A, Russian space engineers prepared to launch a second Salyut, neatly timed to beat Skylab by a month and coincide with the annual May Day celebrations.

The mighty Proton rocket roared heavenwards, marking the resumption of Russia's own manned space programme and signalling to the US that, despite the end of the race to the moon, the battle for colonisation of earth orbit was still open. Up went the big space station, separated from its Proton rocket, then began spinning wildly. As US military radars watched, pieces of the station, including the four solar panels, flew off into space. Salyut 2 was breaking up. Long after the May Day celebrations had finished, Russia's second space station fell back to earth like a giant Roman Candle.

A month later, the last of the Saturn 5 moon rockets took Skylab into orbit, and straight into trouble of its own. During lift-off, part of a protective shield ripped away, taking with it one solar wing and pinning the other to the station's side. Skylab was a crippled bird.

NASA, faced with having to explain away two-and-a-half billion dollars to an apoplectic Congress, went into overdrive. The prognosis was not good. With the solar wings dead, Skylab's only source of electrical power came from four small panels designed to power only the telescope battery above the station. No way could they provide the juice to support three astronauts. Even worse, with the loss of the protective shield, the full glare of the sun was beating down on the stricken ship. The temperature inside Skylab was higher than Death Valley, and rising.

The future for Skylab's crews looked bleak. Within NASA, engineers were talking about the end of the line for the entire manned space venture — unless Skylab could be fixed.

Flight controllers immediately turned the giant space station away from the sun and watched with relief as the needles fell to a tolerable, if sweaty, level. Meanwhile, engineers at the Cape and Houston were brainstorming ways of freeing the damaged wing and providing some protection from the sun.

For the first time, NASA accepted the fact that astronauts would have to fix the ship themselves, by hand if necessary. The manuals and safety procedures were quietly consigned to the waste bins. There was too much at stake.

When Pete Conrad and his crew left the Cape eleven days later, they carried with them two of the weirdest pieces of equipment ever launched into space: a large aluminised plastic 'parasol' and, this being the brainchild of an engineer with a love of sports fishing, a telescopic metal pole with a pair of bolt-cutters welded to one end.

Conrad, short, wiry and irrepressible, was on his fourth space flight. He had flown Gemini 5 for eight days or bust, followed that with Gemini 11, and commanded Apollo 12 to take the runner-up prize for third man on the moon.

Now he was en route for the history books and the 'compleat astronaut' title: the first man to fly Gemini, walk on the moon and rescue a space station. It was the stuff of legend, and Conrad was determined to succeed or die — as well he might — in the attempt.

At launch, Conrad roared 'we can fix anything', and off he went into the ozone, with the fate of NASA resting on his shoulders.

From 270 miles up, Skylab resembled a flying windmill. The workshop and living quarters, constructed from a spare Saturn fuel tank, formed a can-shaped structure out of which, at right angles, came the telescope mount — the windmill's hub — and the four surviving solar panels. These, flashing in the harsh sunlight, looked just the sort of thing Don Quixote would have tilted at.

As they drew closer, the crew could see the jammed solar wing and the blistered exterior of Skylab's body. Conrad inched towards the stricken station while pilot Paul Weitz stood in Apollo's open hatch and tried, unsuccessfully, to cut it free from the debris with his cosmic pruning hook.

Then they tried to dock, and even that was difficult. After nearly a dozen attempts, they made it. When the crew finally cracked the hatch and floated through, it was like being inside a blast furnace. Conrad and his space riggers retreated back to the relative cool of Skylab's main airlock, where they camped out, making occasional scouting trips into the station's interior. On one such trip, Conrad and Weitz managed to push their plastic parasol through a hatch in the station's hull and unfurl it over the workshop area. The third crewman, Joe Kerwin, America's first doctor in space, watched as the

'Up above the world you fly,
Like a windmill in the sky.'
The first Skylab crew survey their battered home (with apologies to Lewis Carroll).

temperature gauges slowly dropped. Now all they had was the power problem, so they went out and fixed *that*.

Conrad and Kerwin clambered round the outside of the flying windmill, nearly three hundred miles above the ground, carrying the pruning hook. As Skylab headed into darkness, the two men clung to the station's hull, waiting for sunrise.

Dawn broke thirty minutes later. The two men struggled to hook their cutters around the debris holding Skylab's surviving solar wing. When finally they succeeded, Conrad handed himself along the cutters' telescopic handle, lashed a line to the jammed wing, and once again they raced into the night. Kerwin, perched on the hull, was the first to catch the faint horizon glow which heralded the approaching sun:

'I can see sunrise, out of China, 'cross the bay, kinda,' quipped the space doctor, full of poesy.

Again they flashed from darkness into light. 'Man, I am really pulling,' groaned Kerwin as he heaved on the cutters.

'Whoops! There she goes!' howled Conrad as the debris parted. Both men strained at the line, then the panel unfolded so fast the shock sent them tumbling to the end of their restraining tethers, whooping and hollering with delight.

'We see amps,' reported the engineers down below. They had fixed it. NASA could breathe again. Now they could settle down to life aboard a space station.

Skylab, together with the docked Apollo ferry, towered twelve storeys high, with a habitable volume that of a large three-bedroomed house. As the 'fix-it' crew floated inside their new home, they drifted through a 17-foot long chamber which housed the telescope controls and the docking equipment, then through the smaller airlock used for spacewalks, then through another hatch, then into the converted Saturn tank which contained the work area and the crew quarters.

The latter, for an astronaut accustomed to the claustrophobic confines of Gemini and Apollo, was breathtaking. It was the biggest space any astronaut or cosmonaut had ever inhabited. The workshop alone was 27 feet long by 22 feet wide, lined with storage tanks and equipment. Past this, and separated from it by a metal lattice-work floor, were the living quarters, with toilet, shower, kitchen (complete with wardroom table), food lockers and sleeping area. Skylab was a true home in space. Since both Conrad and Kerwin were ex-Navy, the workshop was quickly dubbed 'upper deck', the living area 'lower deck'.

Before Skylab, NASA had precious little idea of the long-term effects of life

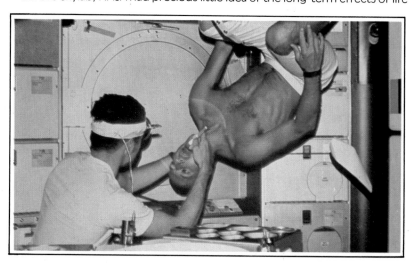

High-flying dentist on the job — Kerwin examines Conrad's teeth without the need for the traditional chair.

in space. The Russians had learnt more from the 18-day flight of Soyuz 9, after which the cosmonauts had to be carried from the capsule; and from the flight of Soyuz 11, from which there were no survivors, than had the Americans with their limited Gemini and Apollo experience.

Could the human body adapt to weightlessness? Would the astronauts return healthy, or would the deterioration, seen on the longer Gemini and Apollo flights, of muscle tissue, bone calcium and the cardiovascular system, render them wheelchair cases on their return?

This, together with 'Can men perform useful work in space to justify the billions of dollars spent in sending them there?' and 'Can men live comfortably in space, or will they flip their lids?' were the questions Skylab had to answer.

So Skylab was a flying laboratory, and the crews were to be its lab rats, watched and controlled by the engineers far below: puppets on a 270-mile string. Their working days were timed to the minute; every gesture and comment was picked up by cameras or tape recorders; every morsel of food logged; every urination and bowel movement measured and stored. Even in their sleep they were bugged as thoroughly as Nixon's White House.

The very size of the workshop, it was thought, might cause the astronauts problems with manoeuvrability and orientation, perhaps leading to the onset of that grim spectre, spacesickness. This notion was quickly dispelled.

In zero-g, men became supermen, able to move the heaviest object effortlessly.

Life in a world without gravity was magical. During one telecast, choreographed to the music of '2001 — A Space Odyssey', the crew sped around the workshop's lockers to build up speed, flipped and cartwheeled around the station, then glided in formation, arms outstretched like cruising birds. Houston applauded the stunts, 'good for at least an Emmy. . . we've just had offers from Ringling Brothers.'

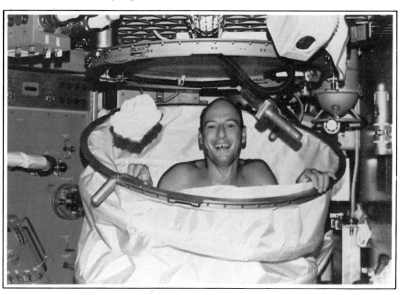

Everyday life aboard a space station. Conrad enjoys a zero-g bath.

Said Conrad: 'We were tickled to death. We never went anywhere straight; we always did a somersault or a flip on the way, just for the hell of it.'

Life wasn't always so much fun. Whenever they opened a drawer, the contents would float out. Liquids emerged from their cans in clouds of droplets that hung like a mist in the air. Then there were the physiological effects on bodies adjusted to gravity. In zero-g, body fluids migrated upwards towards the skull and the astronauts constantly felt as though they were coming down with bad head colds. Sometimes they had nosebleeds.

One side-effect was a change in appearance: cheeks rose, faces flattened. 'Our Chinese look,' commented Conrad.

Conversely, their legs got thinner — 'Little and skinny like crow's legs,' thought Kerwin, who was most interested in the physiological effects of spaceflight. It was Kerwin who discovered the phenomenon of self-oriented perception. He told colleagues on the ground:

> You do have a sense of up and down, and you can change it in seconds, whenever it's convenient to you. If you go from one deck to the other and you're upside down, you say to your brain 'I want that way to be up' and your brain says 'Okay then, that way is up.' It's strictly eyeballs and brain.

Sometimes the real vertical and the brain's vertical clashed, especially when they were upside down with respect to the station. Then they felt uncomfortable, disoriented and even lost. This was most apparent when Kerwin found himself standing on the lower deck ceiling, looking up at the wardroom table, which apparently hung upside down. 'It was bothersome, an Alice in Wonderland feeling,' he said. Such distortion of perception was a part of their magical existence beyond earth's natural laws.

To combat the wasting effect of zero-g, the astronauts exercised regularly on a portable treadmill (real lab rat life, this) and a stationary bicycle. Conrad managed to pedal furiously for ninety minutes, one full orbit, then claimed a new record as the first man to cycle non-stop around the world.

Unlike the Salyut crew, they had no penguin suits and spent much less time keeping fit. Soon Kerwin and Weitz, both on their first space flight, started failing cardiovascular tests, indicating to the medics below that their hearts and circulatory systems had adjusted to weightlessness. Neither felt bad, but the medics worried that they might not be able to re-adjust to earth life. Without gravity to fight against, the astronauts' hearts slowed right down. Conversely, their nervous systems became highly-tuned, sharpening their reflexes to a quick edge. They were adapting to space.

Most of their waking hours were spent hard at work. A battery of telescopes mounted in the 'windmill's' hub had to be trained on the sun for hours at a time. TV monitors inside Skylab allowed the crew to watch in fascination as the sun spewed great gouts of matter into space or frothed and bubbled like a great cauldron. High above earth's atmosphere they were seeing the nearest star as never before.

Other cameras and instruments, including radar, looked down at earth. They measured the height of the ocean waves; mapped ice and snow cover; even made crop inventories and monitored strip mining and land use.

This was merely the tip of an iceberg of experiments, tests, calculations and recordings that the crew had to perform. Sometimes they bitched about having too much to do: 'You got us doing things where we got 89 pieces of gear out and you got us running all over the spacecraft!' complained Conrad.

On their infrequent days off they read, played zero-g darts (made easier by the lack of gravity) or cards, which on occasion drifted off across the wardroom. But mostly they preferred to gaze through the 18 inch wardroom 'porthole' at the continuously unfolding panorama of the planet turning beneath them.

They dined on prime ribs of beef, filet mignon or chicken with gravy — the first astronauts to eat normal food — and then they drifted off into slumber to the sound of music from individual cassette players. Life on board Skylab had little of Apollo's high drama.

The 24-day record of Soyuz 11 was behind them when they finally closed down the space station and headed earthwards. With them went nearly 26,000 sun photographs and 7400 pictures of earth. Conrad, Kerwin and Weitz had spent 28 days in space, breaking all endurance records. They had rescued a busted spaceship and had gone some way towards proving that man could work for long periods outside earth's atmosphere. Most importantly, they were the first crew to return home from a space station alive. Though there was some deterioration in their physiologies (their hearts had shrunk, for one thing) Conrad's crew were in rude good health, and there seemed no reason why the second Skylab crew should not go up for twice as long.

In the summer of 1973, Al Bean, Conrad's old buddy from Apollo 12, took off with two crewmates, two minnows, fifty eggs, six mice, 720 fruit-fly pupae, and two spiders nicknamed Arabella and Anita for company.

The second crew made an immediate entry into the space station, and immediately threw up. They were as sick as dogs for the first days aboard Skylab, and their Apollo ferry fared no better. An entire thruster bank failed, and there was real concern that they would be stranded 270 miles up. For the first time ever, NASA prepared a rescue mission whereby two astronauts would fly a modified Apollo ship, with room for three extra passengers.

It was never needed. The thruster problem was pronounced non-hazardous, and Bean's crew recovered from spacesickness. They were more fortunate than their menagerie: the mice and fruit flies expired via a short circuit. The surviving minnows became, like the crew, completely disordered by the novel experience and swam in tiny loops, while the spiders wove bizarre asymmetrical webs.

The second crew maintained their predecessors' workrate, good humour, and obvious enjoyment of life aboard Skylab. Pilot Jack Lousma brightened up

Garriott outside Skylab.

Welcome home, boys! The second Skylab crew celebrate at Nixon's 'Western White House', San Clemente, applauded by Soviet Premier Brezhnev. Within weeks, Nixon was in disgrace and out of power.

the dull moments by giving impromptu commentaries, over the radio, of selected events, including Bean's haircut:

'Yeah, well, what's going on here? We've needed haircuts for quite a while, so that's what's going on. Here's Captain Alan Bean who's the leader of this mob, and here is the distinguished professor Owen Garriott trimming his hair. . . Well, I can see it's not going to be a professional job, but there's no waiting and the price is right. . . One of the advantages, of course, of having your hair cut in zero gravity is that you don't have to sweep the floor. . . just vacuum it up. Doing a nice job, Owen. You might wonder why we chose Owen to do this job.'

'Yeah, why?' asked Garriott, a moustachioed electrical engineer who always seemed willing to play Lousma's straight man.

'Well, we figured you could always trust a barber with a moustache. Well, we'll come back and check on them later. . . You know there aren't many folks that get their hair cut at eighteen thousand miles an hour. . .'

All Lousma's act lacked was a few appreciative whistles, which was impossible in the low air pressure on board the space station. Indeed, even the astronauts' voices didn't carry very far. They were constantly shouting and, consequently, hoarse.

The second crew hit the water off San Diego in late September. They had travelled twenty-four-and-a-half million miles in 59 days, breaking the previous crew's record, and they were in good health. All systems were go for the third and last visit to Skylab.

Two months later, Gerry Carr, Bill Pogue and Ed Gibson left the Cape, heading towards Skylab and an 80-day voyage. For the first time since the Gemini days of 1966, NASA was flying an all-rookie crew. Their credentials, however, were impressive: Carr, the commander, was an aeronautical engineer; Pogue a former Air Force stunt pilot and mathematician while Gibson, the sole civilian, held a Ph.D in solar physics. All three had been waiting seven years to ride the fire.

And here they were, at last in orbit and heading towards that windmill in the sky. So eager were the third crew to enter the space station that Houston agreed to forgo the planned first night aboard Apollo — which, it was believed, had saved Conrad's crew from spacesickness — and let Carr and his comrades move right in. They felt bad immediately, like tourists who'd had too much excitement too soon.

'Ol' sweaty-palm time there,' said Gibson of Pogue. Pogue vomited. Now they were in a quandary. By rights, they should have radioed Houston immediately. Just before they left earth, however, Congress had debated

Space Shuttle funding, and critics had raised the sensitive issue of space sickness as good reason why Shuttle should be reviewed. Carr and his crew were well aware of this.

'We won't mention the barf,' he offered.

Gibson agreed: 'They're not going to be able to keep track of that.'

Said their miserable co-conspirator, 'It's just between you, me and the couch.'

In that they were badly wrong. Microphones had relayed the entire cover-up to Houston, and Houston was not amused. For the first time, ground reprimanded a crew during a flight — an attitude which the crew resented.

Relations between Houston and the third crew became strained. Conversations were taciturn, they began making mistakes and dropped behind schedule. NASA's response was to load them with more tasks.

In turn, the crew found fault with everything. They complained about the gassy drinking water ('Farting about five hundred times a day is not a good way to go,' grumbled Pogue); they complained about the food, invariably cold and tasteless; they complained about the tableware. Conventional utensils were impractical in zero-g: if an astronaut spooned up some gravy and then had his attention distracted, the gravy would leave the spoon and splatter all over his forehead. They bitched about the toilet, a cabinet mounted halfway up the wall which, festooned with dials and switches, resembled something out of Dr Frankenstein's laboratory. Snarled Pogue: 'I don't know how that was designed, but I'm sure it wasn't by anyone who took a crap and noticed his posture.' They hated the towels (too scratchy), they hated the vacuum cleaner, which never worked properly, and they detested the clothes, which were all one colour. In short, they were completely pissed off.

The more they ranted, the more they fell behind schedule, and the more Houston pushed them to work harder to make up the lost time.

Faced with more tasks than they could accomplish, Carr and his crew became lethargic and negative, especially during the debriefings, during which the astronauts were supposed to be politely candid. The third crew were more than candid — they vented all and every criticism at Houston:

'If you try to be nice,' snarled Pogue, 'it's a crummy debriefing. If you try to be polite or mince words, you emasculate the truth . . . You gotta tell it like it is.'

Without doubt, Carr's crew were the most ill-tempered astronauts ever to ride the fire. Even Wally Schirra paled by comparison.

Finally, bogged down by their impossible workload, the lab rats rebelled. Carr and Pogue grew thick beards which, together with their semi-military coveralls and baseball boots, gave them a distinctly radical appearance. All they lacked were Che Guevara berets. Then they started sleeping late.

Finally, even the blistered ears at ground control allowed that something was wrong.

In the air-clearing which followed, Pogue summed up the problem: 'I'm a fallible human being, I cannot operate at a hundred percent efficiency, I am going to make mistakes. When I tried to operate like a machine, I was a gross failure.'

What an admission for an astronaut! An admission of fallibility!

It was then that NASA learned perhaps its greatest lesson from Skylab, a lesson that would have profound implications for the long-term colonisation of space: that whatever their conditioning and commitment, astronauts were human. They needed time to themselves, even if it meant cutting some science out of the schedules.

Carr's crew had rebelled against the attempt to turn them into machine analogues. By bitching, growing beards and sleeping in, they were signalling to the engineers down below that they were men, not hardware to be pushed whenever the schedules demanded. Screw the schedules! Screw the science!

And so Houston gave the men a free day, and from then on things improved.

'The Revolutionaries' take out the trash. Pogue holds onto the 'ceiling' as he prepares to jump on the trash airlock cover — the only successful method of propelling the trashbags into the waste tank. Carr holds two trash bags. A third hovers.

High above the world, up there all alone, Carr's crew shared with most of their predecessors, astronauts and cosmonauts alike, a feeling of belonging to humanity: the exact antithesis of what the psychologists referred to as the 'cut-off phenomenon'. By pushing them so hard, Houston had effectively isolated the third crew from their world. They were as emotionally deprived as long-term jailbirds.

With the pressure off, Carr and his crewmates sat around the table and stared out the wardroom window. Gibson, try as he might, could see no dividing line between communities or nations. When Carr looked towards the horizon, he was startled by how thin the atmosphere appeared, 'like the skin on an apple', and he became concerned about air pollution. In their own ways, the three men were re-establishing their links with home.

By Christmas, the crew were crashing through the schedules like men possessed. On Christmas Eve, they talked with their families in Houston, showed off a tree fashioned from food containers and discovered presents hidden in the Apollo ferry by their families.

Carr and Pogue spacewalked forth to follow their Christmas Star — Comet Kohoutek, then approaching the sun — and spent seven hours perched on the station's hull, snapping away with hand-held cameras. Said Gibson, who floated out the following day, the yellow and orange comet was 'one of the most beautiful sights in all creation I've ever seen.'

Gibson floats out through Skylab's hatch, spacewalking for a sight of Comet Kohoutek, 'one of the most beautiful sights in all creation . . .'

That spring of 1974, the three men came home. In 84 days, they had covered over 34 million miles, breaking all records for endurance, workrate and fitness. They brought back 75,000 solar snaps and over 40,000 earth pictures of benefit to every 'ology' and 'ography' known to man.

'It's been a good home,' said Gibson as the Apollo ferry backed slowly away. 'I hate to think we're the last guys to use it.'

After their return to earth, the families of all three crews reported that they had difficulty adjusting from the magical to the real world. One morning, said Jack Lousma's wife, he tried to leave a can of shaving foam hanging in mid-air.

It was Lousma who best articulated the astronauts' sense of loss — not from the home world but, like Walt Cunningham on Apollo 7, the unreal but beautiful world of space:

'It's hard to put myself back into Skylab. Sometimes I go over to the Skylab trainer, or I watch the movies we made, but I cannot recreate what it was like. It's almost impossible to recapture now. I never dream about the Skylab. But I often wish I could go that way again.'

While Americans cavorted, worked and argued aboard Skylab, their Russian rivals toiled to repair the damage done by the Soyuz 11 disaster.

In the autumn of '73, two cosmonauts made a simple but successful test flight aboard a much-modified Soyuz, followed by a second. After a two-year hiatus, they were back in business.

By the summer of '74, the Soviet space engineers felt confident enough to lob another Salyut space station into orbit. This time it stayed there.

One thing puzzled the US watchers who tracked Salyut 3 on their big radars: why was Salyut flying fifty miles lower than its predecessors? The question was answered a week later, when Soyuz 14, commanded by Pavel Popovich, who 12 years before had so terrified the Americans as one of the celebrated 'heavenly twins', roared skywards to dock with Salyut 3.

Media coverage of the venture was brief even by Russian standards. Conversation with ground control, monitored by US listening posts, were clipped and in code. American belief that this was no ordinary Salyut was reinforced by pictures taken, by USAF satellites, of geometrical patterns laid out around the Baikonur launch site for the cosmonauts to photograph.

Salyut 3 was a manned spy satellite whose low orbit enabled cosmonauts to observe and record the American war machine. Russia had already demonstrated its ability to destroy enemy spacecraft; to eavesdrop on military radar and radio stations via orbiting electronic spies; and to locate warships from giant nuclear-powered radar satellites. Now the country's space engineers had built and launched the world's first military space station. Again, the Soviet Union was exploiting the 'high ground' of outer space.

Both sides regarded their military satellite fleets as a vital part of the 'electronic battlefield'. If the unthinkable were to happen, the first warnings would come from Ferret eavesdroppers, noting an increase in hostile radio traffic. Spy satellites would snap convoys, activity at missile sites and airfields. Radar craft would detect ships and submarines leaving port. Comsats would direct forces worldwide; navigation satellites would provide pinpoint fixes for retaliation.

Then, early-warning satellites would 'see' missiles leave their silos and submarines vital minutes before ground radar caught them rising above the horizon. It would be left to the comsats to relay messages between the survivors.

The very success of such craft had doomed the Americans' own military man-in-space projects: a small space station using Gemini ships as ferries and a single-seater spaceplane, DynaSoar, which, like Shuttle, would have rocketed into orbit and returned to earth as a supersonic glider. Both projects were scrapped after it had been proved that robots, like the giant 'Big Bird' spy satellite, could do the job just as effectively and for a fraction of the cost.

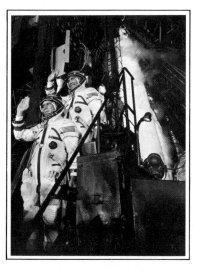

'We who are about to spy salute you!' The crew of Soyuz 14 make their farewells in front of a smoking semyorka.

For once, the US Air Force and the Soviets were in agreement — you don't send a man to do a robot's work.

Russian space engineers couldn't match the superior technology of their rivals, but they possessed a small space station which could be readily adapted to military use. And so Pavel Popovich and his crewmate Yuri Artyukhin spent two weeks prying and spying before returning to earth: the first Salyut cosmonauts to land alive.

In the West, there was none of the hysteria which had gripped the early sixties. The prospect of cosmonauts raining H-Bombs upon the heads of defenceless Americans was a fear of the past: nuclear weapons were banned from space. Besides, the new buzzword was 'detente', and within two years, Americans and Russians would be flying in space together.

Popovich and Artyukhin were the first and last visitors to Salyut 3. The next crew up failed to dock, made a hasty re-entry and the military space station was abandoned.

As 1974 drew to a close, Soviet engineers launched another civilian Salyut and became the first country to orbit two space stations simultaneously. The colonisation of earth orbit had begun.

Within a few weeks, Alexei Gubarev and Georgi Grechko — a civilian designer responsible for the successful Luna soft-landers, now reaping his reward — rode the fire and boarded Salyut 4.

Like Skylab, the accent was on 'useful work'. If cosmonauts wanted to live in space, then they had to pay for the privilege, even if it meant working two full shifts. Gubarev and Grechko toiled for up to twenty hours a day, seven days a week. They studied the sun, planet and stars; they photographed the earth beneath them; they ran experiment after experiment to a schedule that would have appalled the most hearty Skylab astronaut. They were true Stakhanovites in orbit. At the end of the month, the two men returned, haggard and fatigued, but alive. The Soviet engineers who greeted them were convinced that success lay just around the corner.

And so, during the optimistic spring of 1975, Vasily Lazarev and Oleg Makarov left Baikonur for a May Day assignation with Salyut 4. Everything was just fine as the semyorka booster rammed them towards orbit. At the ninety-mile marker, thundering along at 10,000 mph, the Soyuz spaceship suddenly pitched end-over-end. Lazarev and Makarov were heading towards space on the end of a rogue rocket. There was no way they could reach orbit or make a controlled re-entry. Ground controllers fired Soyuz' escape rockets, blasting the frightened cosmonauts away from their raging booster. There they were, in the blackness of space, screaming back to earth along the trajectory of an ICBM warhead. Faster and faster they fell, heading straight towards the Chinese border. The ground controllers could hear them plaintively seeking reassurance that they would not land inside enemy territory, where they could expect a show trial or, even worse, spend the rest of their lives inside a prison camp. Then, as the cabin meter passed 15gs and went off the scale, the two cosmonauts blissfully passed out.

They regained consciousness just as the parachutes opened. It was sunset, and they still had no idea whether they were swinging down towards a heroic welcome or rifle butts. The landing was as bad as the re-entry. Their capsule hit the side of a mountain in the Altai foothills, bumped and crashed down the slope and stopped just yards from the edge of a precipice, where rescue teams found them, thankfully just inside Russian territory.

The flight, from launch to landing, lasted less than 5 minutes. Lazarev and Makarov were alive, barely. Their injuries ranged from broken ribs to internal bleeding and severe concussion. Lazarev, the eldest, was hurt so badly he never flew again. Makarov, displaying what most people would regard as foolhardy courage, recovered to ride the fire a second time.

It was not a good time for a serious space failure. The planned Soviet-American 'handshake in space' was just three months away, and US critics were firing away at their new partners' competence, which was described as

Soyuz 18 goes down the tracks. Foreground, the semyorka; centre, the launchpad with gantry arms down; background, the flame trench and Kazakhstan steppes. Minutes after launch, the crew — Vasily Lazarev and Oleg Makarov — were heading towards space on the end of a runaway booster. They survived — barely.

'primitive' or, less politely 'plain, goddamned brute-force engineering.' Many agreed with Senator William Proxmire when he argued that any Russian failure could jeopardise the lives of American astronauts. Soviet engineers hastily assured their American counterparts that the semyorka used to launch Lazarev and Makarov was an old model, but the doubts remained.

Three years had passed since President Richard M. Nixon made his heady visit to Moscow and proclaimed a new era of Soviet-American co-operation, of which the joint space flight was the PR clincher. Nixon was in disgrace after the Watergate revelations and his stand-in, Gerald Ford, was mopping up after the fall of Saigon and the consequent humiliation of American martial prowess.

Anything concerned with Nixon was under suspicion: especially when it involved Russian access to American technology. What began as a glorious 'space handshake' was now seen as a 'billion-dollar giveaway.'

'Our arms round their shoulders and their hands in our pockets,' was how one US space official viewed the American position. Others were more sanguine: the Apollo hardware was ten years old, and the Soviets could buy NASA technical reports anyway. The only new piece of hardware involved in the flight was the docking system which would allow the two crews to meet, and that was no big deal.

So Apollo-Soyuz went ahead. If anyone benefited, it was NASA who, as *Time* magazine pointed out, needed the Russians 'if only to keep alive the badly curtailed US manned space programme.'

NASA poster celebrates Apollo-Soyuz, 'detente in space', the mission cooked up between Nixon and Brezhnev to symbolise the end of the Cold War. Clockwise from the emblem: Stafford, Slayton and Brand; then the Russian crew, Kubasov and his commander, the veteran cosmonaut Alexei Leonov.

Both sides made the maximum PR out of the venture — here the Russian crew face the world's press.

For the engineers, it was the first chance since the beginning of the space race to check out their rivals' hardware and systems. As they sniffed around each other like wary dogs, both sides were fascinated. The Russians were bemused by NASA's ability to spend a thousand bucks where ten would do. They were even more shocked by the layoffs and cutbacks after Apollo and Skylab, the waste of skilled people and expensive hardware.

In turn, the Americans were amazed by what they found at Baikonur. The Soyuz launchpad was the same as it had been nearly twenty years ago, when Sputnik 1 thundered into the heavens. So was the semyorka rocket — an uprated version of Korolev's old R-7 missile, archaic by American standards. Soyuz itself, far from being a glittering display of Soviet technology, had no computer, no internal guidance system and no proper navigation platform. Soyuz pilots relied on automatic controls or ground controls: to dock with Salyut, the entire space station had to be lined up with the approaching ferry. No pilot control! No Buck Rogers flying skills! No wonder the Russians had lost the moon race!

There was just no way a Soyuz could have performed the complex manoeuvres required during a lunar voyage, let alone returned its pilot safely home. Much to their chagrin, the NASA engineers realised that they had been suckered. All those years of imagined Soviet superiority! They had seen shadows and imagined Golems.

As far as the astronauts were concerned, this was the last flight out. Shuttle was way off in the future, and many of them would not be around when the spaceplane flew. Leading the field for a place aboard Apollo was Deke Slayton, the last active Mercury veteran and the only one of those original space heroes without a flight to his name. Heart trouble grounded him just eight weeks before he was due to fly back in 1962. Since then, Slayton had bossed the astronaut office, selecting crews from Gemini to Apollo. Now, with a clean bill of health, he was about to add his own name to the roster. No-one complained. At the age of 52, it was Slayton's last chance before he was eligible for Social Security. Apollo's commander, Tom Stafford, was another old-timer with three space flights to his credit. At the age of 45, Stafford's hopes of flying Shuttle were slim. The third crew member was Vance Brand, a rookie.

As far as personality went, the Americans were outshone by Soyuz commander Alexei Leonov, world's first spacewalker and a bona fide Soviet hero. The son of a miner, Leonov could hold his own at any social gathering, as comfortable chatting to presidents as he was with his close buddies. He was friendly, flamboyant, painted romantic sci-fi space canvases and appeared to have a limitless capacity for vodka and partying.

Ironically, it was the cosmonauts who regarded Apollo-Soyuz as an excuse for a solid programme of revelry, while the Americans tried to get some serious training done. The crews would visit one another's headquarters — Houston and Star City, outside Moscow — for mutual briefing sessions. At Star City, these were invariably followed by drinking-and-dining parties hosted by the cosmonauts, during which fearsome quantities of vodka would be hoisted. Afterwards, the shattered astronauts would concede defeat and retreat unsteadily to the safety of their bugged hotel rooms. The problem was finally solved by appointing a 'duty drunk', whose function was to match Leonov and his cronies toast for toast while his fellows would empty their glasses into the nearest potted palm.

During their visits to America, the cosmonauts spent most of their time on the cocktail circuit, handling ceremonials and fancy dinners with a facility the tongue-tied astronauts could only admire. Between glad-handing, Leonov and his buddies spent as much time as possible hunting, waterskiing and racing fast cars. Socially, they had the Americans licked.

The two crews found much common ground: 'We're all test pilots, and test pilots are all alike,' said Slayton. 'They love to fly and they hate doctors.'

On 15 July, 1975, Alexei Leonov and Valeri Kubasov made the first live-on-TV

Leonov (left) and Kubasov relax. Keeping up with Leonov's limitless capacity for enjoyment posed as much of a problem for the Americans as the technical aspects of the flight.

'Alas, poor Yorick' — Slayton as a Mercury astronaut. Grounded by heart trouble back in 1962, Slayton was the only one of the 'original 7' to miss out on a flight. Now, it was Slayton's last chance to ride the fire before retirement.

'Tovarich!' Despite the politics, Apollo-Soyuz was a genuine success — and the first time the two great space powers met on equal terms. Even so, it was a temporary hiatus in the space race. Here, Alexei Leonov, upside down, pays a flying visit to Apollo.

launch from Baikonur. Seven hours later, the last Saturn 1 rocket took off from the Cape, carrying the last Apollo and the docking equipment. To save money, the launch crew was fired immediately.

'Man, I tell you,' exulted Slayton, 'this is worth waiting sixteen years for.' They were en route for the great space handshake.

TV viewers down below saw the pawn-shaped Soyuz coming slowly out of the blackness, sunlight glinting off its wing-like solar panels.

Then the word came from Houston:

'Moscow is go for docking. Houston is go for docking. It's up to you guys to set 'em up. Have fun.'

As Leonov held Soyuz steady, the radio crackled with Russian and American voices counting off instrument readings and instructions. Stafford nosed the more manoeuvrable Apollo towards the Russians. Then, 140 miles above the Atlantic, the two ships docked.

'Soyuz and Apollo are shaking hands!' cried Leonov in his heavily accented English. 'Good show!'

It took the crews three hours to prepare for what *Time* called 'High-altitude, high-budget diplomatic theater carefully scripted for maximum political impact.' They were to meet inside the docking module, which involved cracking and sealing hatches; changing atmospheres; and checking TV cameras and radio circuits. Finally, Alexei Leonov poked his head past Soyuz' hatch and, at Stafford's urging, squirmed through to join the astronauts.

Stafford greeted him in Russian with a strong mid-west burr which the cosmonauts called 'Oklahomski':

'Tovarich!'

'Very happy to see you,' replied a beaming Leonov. 'How are things?'

And then the two men shook hands and exchanged bearhugs. They were joined by Slayton and Kubasov (Brand rode shotgun in Apollo) and traded flags and presents, while Houston relayed fulsome congratulations from Party chief Brezhnev — 'a new page in history' — and caretaker President Ford, who chatted away like a TV talk-show host. Inside Soyuz, they shared a meal, during which Tom Stafford bolted down three tubes of soggy borscht — plastered over with vodka labels by Leonov — only to resort to Lomotil pills later. Said

Leonov about their respective cuisines: 'Your food is slop, and our food is slop.'

Two days later, the glorious meeting of the Cold War space rivals — and the world's most expensive political gesture — was over. But the last American splashdown was very nearly the final curtain for the three astronauts. At twenty-four thousand feet, Apollo filled with acrid fumes. As the capsule swung gently down towards the water, Vance Brand passed out as his crewmates struggled, choking, to reach their oxygen masks. It was total chaos. Their radio link with the outside world garbled all attempts to communicate with the bemused Navy frogmen outside the window, they were upside-down in their straps, and the capsule was rocking and rolling in the heavy swell.

'Get this fucking hatch open!' screamed Stafford as Slayton tried desperately to revive Brand. Finally, he cracked the hatch himself, and the three men fell, retching, into the arms of the frogmen. For the benefit of the cameras, they put on a brave face, smiling and waving, then headed straight for the sickbay.

The last Apollo crew had missed serious injury by seconds. On the way down, Brand missed throwing two vital switches and some of the highly corrosive oxidiser had been sucked into the cabin. Despite all the reservations about the Russians' ability to fly a safe mission, it was the Americans who had screwed up. What had started as an expensive space triumph had nearly ended in tragedy.

Two days after the near-fatal splashdown, the Russians announced a new Soviet space endurance record. Pyotr Klimuk and Vitali Sevastyanov had racked up 61 successful days aboard Salyut 4, and had returned safely and in rude good health.

It was deeply galling for NASA. The Russians, despite their 'plain, goddamned brute-force engineering,' were flying crew after crew, making all the breakthroughs in earth orbit, while all the Americans could do was look towards Shuttle, way off in the future. The victors of the moon race had become runners-up in the competition to colonise the edge of space.

America's consolation prize came in the spider-like form of Viking 1 which, exactly seven years to the day since Neil Armstrong planted a tentative space boot on the moon, became the first spacecraft to land intact on the surface of Mars.

It was another giant leap for robotkind and, as it coincided with America's bicentennial celebrations, was cause for much patriotic chest-beating. The Stars and Stripes on Mars, the Red Planet!

The Vikings (a second lander touched down several weeks later) carried two scanners, a meteorological station and, most importantly, two complete

Moscow welcomes the Apollo-Soyuz crews. (left to right) Stafford, Leonov, Brand, Kubasov and Slayton.

biochemistry labs which, it was hoped, would solve the question — is there life on Mars?

Back on earth, the scientists eagerly awaited the first news from the Red Planet.

The first photos showed a barren, rock-strewn landscape with not a single Martian in sight. Mars was pretty — a reddish-orange landscape beneath a creamy orange-pink sky — but apparently lifeless.

The Red Planet's atmosphere was largely carbon dioxide, its temperature far below freezing, and its surface contained an abundance of iron oxides. It was a cold, rusty planet.

Though the biochemistry labs found some activity in the Martian 'soil', there was no evidence of life — not so much as a microbe. Neither was there any evidence of long-dead civilisations. Martians, it appeared, were but the figments of earthly imaginations.

Not everyone was fooled by the Vikings. A clairvoyant claimed that Viking 1 had landed weeks before the official announcement, but the US Government had suppressed the news — because the Martians were annoyed and were about to retaliate.

The Vikings not only hammered another nail into the coffin of romance. Again, spacecraft had proved that they could explore the planets for a fraction of the cost of a human expedition, without risk. It was no longer considered reasonable to send a man to do a robot's job.

Viking looks at Mars — a dead red planet beneath an orange sky. Said Viking scientist Gerald Soffen: 'All the signs suggest that life exists on Mars, but we can't find any bodies.'

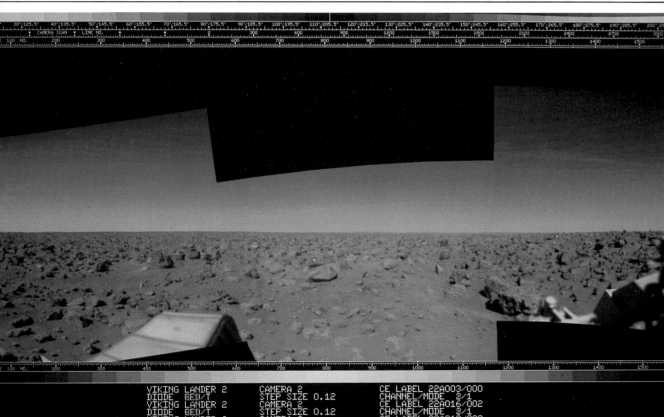

CHAPTER TEN

DACHAS IN THE SKY

IT HAD taken the Russians four years to convert the Soyez 11 tragedy into the 'successes' of Salyut 4, from which cosmonauts had returned to earth alive, even if there were some near misses along the way. Had their luck changed? Had the perseverance and the money—$6 billion a year—finally paid off? Was this, at last, the age of the space station?

As America's Vikings approached Mars in the summer of 1976, yet another military Salyut thundered into orbit. A two-man crew followed shortly, aiming to break Skylab's 84-day record, only to return prematurely after the station's air conditioning system ran amok. They were more fortunate than the next crew, who failed to dock, made a hasty late-night re-entry and ended up in the freezing waters of Lake Tengiz, Siberia.

By the time Viking 1 landed, a Russian crew was at last aboard Salyut 5, where they stayed for nearly three weeks.

On 29 September, 1977, six weeks after Salyut 5 took the long plunge towards a fiery death above the Pacific, yet another Soviet station left Baikonur en route for the edge of space and, yet again, the first crew failed to dock, fell back to earth and landed in a cornfield.

It was the old pattern repeated: glorious achievement followed by dismal failure. Out of nine manned Salyut flights, one crew was dead and four had made emergency landings. If space stations were the wave of the future, then cosmonauts rode that wave at their peril.

As 1977 drew to a close, another Soyuz rose out of Baikonur and streaked towards the new station, Salyut 6. On board were Yuri Romanenko, a space rookie, and Georgi Grechko, whose knowledge of spacecraft design and experience with Salyut 4 would, it was hoped, enable him to beat the Salyut jinx.

Salyut 6 boasted two docking ports, one at either end of the 20-ton station. The first crew had, unsuccessfully, attempted to dock at the forward port, so Romanenko aimed at the aft port and berthed flawlessly.

They were aboard the most expensive and sophisticated Soviet space station ever built. As well as the two docking ports, Salyut 6 featured an

Salyut 6 crew Romanenko and Grechko before their epic flight. The Soviets — losers in the moon race — were riding the crest of the new wave: space stations.

autopilot — on earlier stations cosmonauts spent one hour in every three just keeping the ship on the right heading — a computer-controlled navigation platform, and a redesigned electrical system.

Like Skylab, the station was a collection of cylinders which, from the outside, resembled a fat telescope with wings. They floated through the largest 'can', which was around 14 feet in diameter and contained most of the scientific equipment and the 'mini-gym', then entered the 10-ft diameter living-room-cum-workshop. Ahead of them was the smallest can, housing an airlock and the forward docking port. The whole complex was about the size of a mobile home and was packed full of stores, control panels, equipment and life-support systems, so there was barely room to swing a cat, let alone indulge in the zero-g acrobatics possible in the much larger Skylab.

The cosmonauts spent the first week checking out their new home. Then it was time to inspect the forward docking port which had caused the first crew so much disappointment. Grechko, the engineer, spacewalked along the outside of Salyut, prodded and poked around the port, could find nothing wrong, and turned back towards the access hatch. He was astonished to see Romanenko, who should have remained inside the hatchway, floating off into space, his tether flapping behind him. In his eagerness and excitement, the young cosmonaut had completely forgotten to fasten his line. Romanenko was spinning off into the void.

Grechko launched himself off Salyut, made a frenzied grab at the passing tether, managed to hold it and pulled his gasping crewmate back to safety. Worse was yet to come: inside the airlock, the shaken cosmonauts found that

Cosmonauts-eye view of Salyut 6, the first true space station. A pawn-shaped Progress supply ship (right) has already docked with the 20-ton station. The inbound Soyuz ferry will now have to dock at the forward airlock, to the left of Salyut's large solar panels.

the vent valve appeared to be jammed open. If they tried to crack the inner hatch, Salyut's atmosphere would empty into space like the air from a pricked balloon. They were effectively marooned: locked out of their house in space.

Grechko pondered the problem. There was no alternative except to spacewalk to the other end of the station and try to force their way inside the Soyuz ferry which, since it was designed to withstand the rigours of re-entry, was built like a bank vault. They had to risk the hatch or die. It was that jinx again.

So the two men gingerly cranked the airlock open. The pressure held. They were safe — it was a faulty meter, not the valve.

From then on, everything went as planned. They had, it seemed, beaten the jinx. They celebrated the New Year around a fir tree, and looked forward to the arrival of visitors.

On 11 January, 1978, another Soyuz docked at the spare forward port, carrying two cosmonauts, mail, newspapers and fresh food. Though the psychologists had pushed for regular visits as a means of reducing isolation, there was a more pressing reason than mere companionship.

Like any other piece of machinery, spacecraft became less reliable as they grew older. The lifetime of a Soyuz was reckoned to be around 100 days at most. The solution was to fly another crew to the station, swap ships, return in the old craft and leave the residents a gleaming new Soyuz.

It was another Soviet space first: a true three-ring circus in orbit. To test the rigidity of the new complex, the cosmonauts were instructed to jump up and down, which they did with great enjoyment, bouncing from floor to roof like Olympic trampolinists.

The visit was all too short. Five days later, Romanenko and Grechko were once again alone in space.

Since the new Soyuz ferry was docked forward, the aft port was now free, and within a week the cosmonauts had new company — a robot.

Skylab was designed as a strictly self-contained space station. Once the fuel, water and oxygen ran out, so did the life of the station. There was no provision for re-supply. Even as Romanenko and Grechko toiled, the big space station was drifting through space, a spent hulk slowly falling towards the stratosphere.

But NASA's Soviet counterparts had different ideas about the design and purpose of space stations. With fewer technical resources and no equivalent to the massive Saturn 5 rocket — their own G-1 project had long since been mothballed — the Russian designers aimed for a smaller space station which could be re-supplied by cheap unmanned cargo ships.

Oleg Makarov leaves his wife to ride the fire again. No ordinary farewell this — on his previous flight, Makarov narrowly missed death after landing out of control near the Chinese border. Happily, this flight ends normally.

Soyuz 28, carrying Vladimir Remek — the first spaceman from outside Russia or America — awaits launch. Russia still benefits from the legacy of Korolev: Soyuz, semyorka and launchpad are all examples of the 'Chief Designer's' genius.

Romanenko and Grechko watched through one of Salyut's many portholes as the first Progress nosed towards them, thrusters firing and beacons flashing. The 26-ft robot carried drinking water, a new TV set, replacement equipment and, most important of all, rocket fuel.

The refuelling task was both hazardous and time-consuming. It took them four days to pump barely a ton of the volatile liquid into Salyut's tanks and to unload and store the cargo. Before Progress 1 was undocked and sent to a fiery death, the cosmonauts loaded it full of garbage. Ground control then fired the cargo ship's own engine to boost Salyut into a higher orbit.

The Soviet engineers had taken a great leap forward in the colonisation of earth orbit. If Salyuts could be endlessly re-supplied by Progress ships, the stations' lifetimes extended by using the robots as space tugs while cosmonauts shuttled regularly into orbit aboard Soyuz ferries, then the old science-fiction dream of a permanent base above the atmosphere was coming true.

A fortnight before they were due to return home, Romanenko and Grechko received more visitors, one of whom was a new breed of cosmonaut — the 'guest'.

Vladimir Remek was a Czech, the first man from outside Russia or America to fly in space, and his presence aboard Salyut gave the Russians another propaganda point over their rivals. It was good politics to fly 'guest' cosmonauts from brother socialist countries. The Americans were talking about flying Europeans on Shuttle, but that was way off in the future. In the meantime, the Russians could afford to offer a place on Soyuz to politically reliable candidates from other countries — Remek's father was Deputy Defence Minister — as long as a Russian flew the spacecraft and the 'guest' kept well out of the way.

So there they were, three Russians and a Czech, flying along in international harmony, when Romanenko and Grechko passed Skylab's 84-day record and entered the history books.

The Americans were good losers. Carr, Gibson and Pogue telegraphed their congratulations, just as the Russians had greeted the first moon landing. As far as space stations were concerned, the Soviet Union was number one.

On 16 March, 1978, after spending 96 days in earth orbit, Romanenko and Grechko came back to earth. They were in good health, and the flight doctors could find nothing out of the ordinary except a tendency for the cosmonauts to 'swim' out of bed in the mornings.

Salyut 6 stayed empty for only three months before another crew moved in and set up house. Vladimir Kovalyonok, the commander, had already come within a few feet of Salyut 6 on the first abortive flight. Now he and his partner, rookie Alexander Ivanchenkov, were there to stay.

They adjusted to zero-g with ease. Soviet flight doctors, working from the experience of earlier flights, knew that the onset of weightlessness, combined with the sheer hard work involved in docking and the emotional stress of adapting to life on the edge of space, made every hour seem like a day. The idea, they said, was 'to enter the cosmic rhythm without rushing.'

The Photons (each flight had a personal callsign) worked at their own pace and took plenty of time off to watch videotapes on their TV, read, or listen to music. Ivanchenkov regretted not taking his guitar with him: ground control promised to stow it aboard a Progress.

There were regular telecasts from orbit, relayed on Moscow TV:

'Dear viewers,' broadcast Kovalyonok, 'we've been spinning around the earth, circle by circle, watching the planet and thinking how wonderful and small it is.'

He then took his audience on a tour of the station, pausing at the control desk:

'The impression made by this immense complex beginning to submit to your decision, to your will, is gripping — just a millimetre's movement of the control stick, and the station starts to obey.'

It may not have been the 'Wally, Walt and Donn Show,' but the viewers loved it.

For a week or so, Salyut's orbit was adjusted to keep it out of the earth's shadow, giving the Photons a unique view of a cosmos in which the sun never rose nor set, but just rolled around the horizon, bathing the station continuously in bright light. This put the environmental system under great strain: on an earlier Salyut 4 flight, the humidity rose to such an extent that the cosmonauts complained bitterly to an unsympathetic ground control.

'The windows are still fogged over,' they protested. 'And the green mould — it's halfway up the wall! Can't we come home now?'

'No!'

The Photons had an ample supply of fans to keep the heat tolerable.

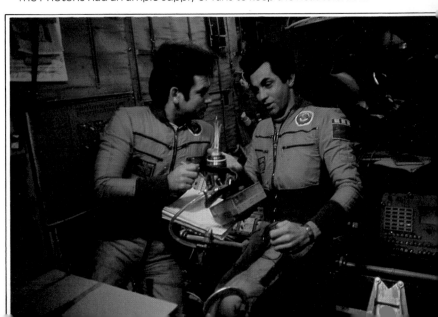

Romanenko (right) and partner aboard Salyut. After nearly a hundred days in space, the two men passed Skylab's record, returning to earth in good health. Soviet spacemen were learning how to survive the zero-g barrier.

Like Skylab, the station had a wardroom, shower, dining table and toilet. Again, psychologists did the interior decorating — soft pastels for a homely atmosphere — which the Salyut crews learned to live with.

The cuisine was impressive: a different menu every day, with steak, chicken, a choice of breads, tinned ham, soups and jams, cheese and fruit. This diet was supposed to be supplemented with fresh vegetables from a miniature hydroponic garden — onions, cucumbers, tomatoes, carrots, garlic and mushrooms — but, try as they might, the Photons seemed to lack green fingers. The best they could achieve was a few onions and mushrooms, which they fell upon with much lip-smacking. Weightlessness seemed to have a strange effect on the taste buds. Favourite foods seemed to lose their flavour, tasting like sawdust, while childhood dislikes suddenly acquired the delights of manna.

To establish feelings of emotional security, the Photon's day ran on Moscow time, the air-conditioning was dosed with pine-scented air fresheners, and they had regular two-way TV chats with their families. The psychologists held more power within the Salyut team than they ever had at Houston: videotapes of concerts and films were provided, along with books and a chess set.

Mission Control piped up music while the Photons worked — especially during the hours-long exercise routines, which were intense and monotonous beyond belief. Film stars, sports personalities and Moscow literati were televised, live, for the Photon's amusements. The aim was to have lively cosmonaut minds in healthy cosmonaut bodies: even if it meant wearing clumsy penguin suits twelve hours a day.

Most of their waking hours were spent at work. As well as the purely scientific experiments, the Photons laboured at commercial tasks, of which the two most important were earth photography and smelting.

The former involved snapping away at the ground beneath them with a special Zeiss camera which exposed film to selected bands of the visible

The view from Salyut: the 'eye' of Cyclone Rita from the station's porthole as both cyclone and spacecraft pass over South-East Asia.

(inset) Visitors to a used space station: the Photons play host to a new crew. While the Russians explored the 'new frontier' of earth orbit, their rivals wrestled with Shuttle. Even worse for the Americans was the fact that the hulk of Skylab was tumbling, out of control, shortly to crash into the Pacific.

spectrum and part of the infrared. Specialists back in Russia would analyse the returned film and determine everything from thermal pollution in lakes to mineral deposits and even the type, extent and health of crops. Another camera was used to make precise geological maps. One picture, if it showed the location of a new copper lode, could be worth millions of roubles. From their vantage point on the edge of space, cosmonauts could provide more knowledge about Siberia, the Soviet Union's vast and unexplored frontier, than an army of scientists — for a fraction of the cost.

There were two furnaces aboard Salyut. One, dubbed Splav, used zero-g to create new metal alloys for use in high-technology equipment. The other, Krystall, exploited the same property to create monocrystal films for high-speed computers, semiconductor crystals of flawless perfection and an entire range of optical glass of a purity earthbound scientists could only dream about.

Some of the work was experimental, but much of the Photons' time was devoted to filling orders from Soviet factories. Salyut 6 was becoming a high-precision, high-technology outpost of the Russian economy. One batch of semiconductor material was worth $8000 a gram, and there were plenty of

grammes. The Russians had found the diamonds of space: not on the moon, nor on Mars, but right there in earth orbit.

Towards the end of June, the Photons hosted their first visitors. These were Pyotr Klimuk, a space station veteran, and a Polish 'guest'. They were greeted by the Photons with bread and salt in the traditional fashion, and then the four men unloaded the new Soyuz and went back to work.

Ten days later, the visitors rocketed back to earth, taking with them hundreds of photos of Polish territory and 47 grammes of the precious semiconductor. It may not have paid for the flight, but it helped.

Not all of the Salyut workload was for civilian use. Much of the hi-tech produce went to the military. Optics used in the various sensors and telescopes were later transferred to spy satellites, and the cosmonauts tested tracking and early-warning hardware. Like NASA, the Russian space engineers needed military support to prise roubles from their cost-conscious bosses.

Kovalyonok and Ivanchenkov left Salyut 6 on 2 November, 1978. They had spent just under 140 days in space. In those four-and-a-half months, the Photons took 20,000 earth photos; completed 50 smelting experiments — an output which, stated Moscow, equalled a year's work from a terrestrial factory; had received and unloaded three Progress tenders; spacewalked over Japan; and played host to two visiting Soyuz crews.

The touchdown was covered live by Moscow TV, and viewers watched in astonishment as the two cosmonauts walked unaided from the descent module.

At the welcoming triumph in Moscow's Red Square, Party leader Brezhnev lead the orations:

'Comrades! The successful carrying out of the longest spaceflight in history, known throughout the world, is a mighty victory for Soviet science, knowledge and skill, and the will and heroism of the Soviet party!'

In just one short year, the Soviet Union had flown ten successful missions to Salyut 6; had racked up record after record; had introduced a cheap, reliable robot cargo ship which could keep crews resupplied for weeks at a time; and had paved the way towards the profitable exploitation of earth orbit. Not since the halcyon days of Gagarin and Tereshkova had the future looked so bright for the Soviet conquest of space.

The return to earth and a normal life. 'Several minutes before our landing,' said Ivanchenkov, 'wind rushed into our cabin. Forgetting about the seat belts, we both bent forward towards the earth's air. Later, when we stepped on the ground, we were literally intoxicated by the fresh wind.'

While the Russians were full of pride and hope, the mood at NASA was gloomy. The first Space Shuttle, Columbia, should have made its maiden flight. Instead, America's reusable spaceplane was sitting in a hangar at Lancaster, California, millions of dollars over budget and years behind schedule.

Shuttle had gone bad from the beginning. The heady blank-cheque days of Apollo were over, and NASA had been forced to settle for the cheapest system the engineers could devise. Even then, it was only the intervention of the Pentagon that had persuaded Congress to shell out five billion bucks for the project.

Building Shuttle would be easy, NASA assured its reluctant backers. The engineers would simply assemble some state-of-the-art hardware, strap it to a pair of big boosters, and fire it off into the heavens.

The actual building of Columbia posed no great problems. Although it was designed to fly at a speed guaranteed to terrify the most hardened air traveller, in size and shape it was no different from a commercial jet liner. Outside the atmosphere, of course, Columbia would metamorphose into a spaceship, but NASA had twenty years of experience in designing spaceships. The two big solid rocket boosters were scaled-up versions of a proven Air Force launcher, and the fuel tank, which Columbia would ride piggy-back, was simply a giant metal can.

NASA's nightmare concerned Columbia's heatshield and its three main engines.

No-one had ever constructed a reusable heatshield. From Gagarin onwards, astronauts and cosmonauts had relied upon thick layers of shielding to protect them from the furnace of re-entry. As the temperature built up, so the white-hot layers sloughed off into the stratosphere, carrying heat with them. By the time the space-travellers landed, most of the heatshield had burned away.

Since Columbia would fly and fly again, the heatshield had to be a permanent fixture. NASA engineers decided to cover Columbia's wings and underbelly with thousands of ceramic tiles, each one individually designed and machined. They were perfect heat-haters. One side of the tile could be red-hot, the other cool enough to touch.

It became the most expensive tiling job in history.

The machining and fixing of each tile took weeks. Wind tunnel tests showed tiles would fall off during the stress of re-entry, so they were replaced. Some tiles just wouldn't fit. To catch up with the receding schedule, the contractors hired more tilers. Up went the cost.

Meanwhile, Columbia's engines were driving the engineers crazy.

There were three of them, and they were the lightest, most powerful rocket engines ever designed. Each engine alone packed more thrust than John Glenn's Atlas booster. They also had to throttle up and down like an auto engine, and run on high-performance liquid hydrogen. With NASA's budget, it was like trying to build a Cadillac for the price of a Volkswagen.

The result was failure after failure: turbine blades, pumps, seals, bearings, fuel injectors and valves exploded, seized up or refused to work. Because of the lack of money, spares were few and far between. There was no time to test each part individually, so the entire engine had to be stripped down and rebuilt. One engine, $25 million worth of high-technology, was a complete write-off.

It was the worst series of breakdowns and delays since the Vanguard days, and there was even talk of handing the whole Shuttle programme over to the Air Force, which would have meant the demise of the Agency. By 1979, Shuttle was two years behind schedule and two billion dollars in the red. Even within NASA, Columbia was referred to as a 'space lemon'.

The one consolation for NASA was that the dummy spaceplane, Enterprise, had come through its glide tests with flying colours. Named after the more successful spaceship of 'Star Trek' fame — a small concession to public

Jupiter, greatest of the planets, from Voyager. Between spacecraft and planet lie two moons, one over the mysterious Red Spot. The spectacular success of the robot missions to Jupiter and Saturn hammered the final nail into the coffin of romance. Men would never venture to the outer planets: spacecraft could explore for a fraction of the cost, without risk. Within NASA, Voyager was the last great planetary venture. The money was needed to bail out Shuttle.

relations by the agency — Enterprise was dropped off the back of a 747 Jumbo jet and made several perfect landings on the long runway at Edwards AFB, California, just a few miles away from Columbia's hangar. There were no doubts that a pilot could land the 100-ton glider, but would it ever get off the ground?

Despite the success of Voyager, the outlook for planetary exploration looked grim. NASA was draining money from its other projects to shore up Shuttle. Said one scientist: 'space science is in shambles. Planetary science is in shambles.'

NASA's plan to map the solar system — using robots that had proved their worth and by doing so denying astronauts the chance to visit Mars and beyond — were about to be killed off so that men could once again fly to the edge of space. If the space scientists appreciated the irony, they were not amused.

By the middle of 1979 Columbia had fallen so far behind schedule that NASA offered impatient customers flights on throwaway rockets: the very boosters Shuttle was supposed to replace. July should have been a time of great celebration, the tenth anniversary of Neil Armstrong's moon landing. Instead, three of Armstrong's contemporaries accused NASA of cutting corners and risking the lives of the first crew. It was a vote of no confidence, and it raised the spectre of a repeat of the Apollo 204 disaster.

At the end of the year, Columbia finally arrived at the Cape. Thousands of tiles were missing. Again the schedule slipped, again NASA went cap in hand for more bucks, and again the Pentagon came to the rescue.

Secretary of Defense Harold Brown declared Shuttle essential to future US military planning, and Congress dipped deep.

The Pentagon had wanted a manned military space programme ever since the generals decided space was to be the new 'high ground'. Now they were near to realising that dream. Over half the planned Shuttle flights would carry USAF cargo, and workmen were already building a massive new USAF Shuttle launch complex on the Californian coast. Even Columbia's design had been influenced by the Pentagon, who wanted a larger cargo bay to house the USAF's huge spy satellites. NASA had needed the military to push Shuttle past Congress, and the agency was paying the price. The days when NASA could claim to be a civilian outfit were over.

By March 1981, NASA was ready to launch Columbia. It was three years late, cost nearly double, and had taken longer to build than the entire Apollo project from Kennedy's historic speech to Armstrong's footprint. And the troubles were still not over: during an overhaul, a technician was asphyxiated. It was the first death at the Cape since Apollo 204.

Worse was to come.

Russia, said the Pentagon, was building its own Shuttle.

CHAPTER ELEVEN

THE WIDE BLACK YONDER

WHILE AMERICA agonised over its 'space lemon', Vladimir Kovalyonok rode the fire a third time. His companion was Viktor Savinykh, the world's 100th space traveller, and they were flying the latest 'T' series Soyuz, a ship as sophisticated as anything astronauts had ever flown.

Salyut 6 had changed since Kovalyonok last visited. The walls were covered with posters and mementos — even a Buddha-like statue of Lenin — and equipment brought up by Progress ferries filled the workshop and wardroom. Salyut 6 had the used, funky look of a station that had served its time.

Back in 1977, the station was reckoned to have a life of two years. No-one had anticipated that Salyut 6 would survive so long: Kovalyonok's earlier flight was supposed to have been the last mission, yet here he was again, complaining to Mission Control that there was no room to stow their new gear.

During the intervening two-and-a-half years, crew after crew lived aboard Salyut, supplied by regular Progress flights. Setting endurance records became a game of the past: cosmonaut Valeri Ryumin spent a total of nearly one year in orbit. Cosmonauts learned a new discipline, the care and maintenance of a used space station. As well as installing new equipment, they could now repair ageing units, extending the life of the station

Valeri Ryumin, sporting zero-g hairstyle, fights to untangle spaghetti-like wiring. Ryumin, destined to spend over a year in space, found the experience alarming: 'Looking into the mirror I fail to recognise myself. I feel dizzy, nauseous. My movements lack coordination. I keep bumping into things, mostly with my head . . . Chaos in a teapot!'

The green, green grass of home. (left to right) Ryumin and crewmate Lyakhov sample the delights of earth after their record-breaking flight.

America rejoins the space race. (left to right) Crippen and veteran space pilot Young with Shuttle model before Columbia's maiden flight.

indefinitely. Whenever atmospheric drag lowered Salyut's orbit, Progress ferries would boost it back up. While Salyut 6 couldn't be termed a true permanent manned base on the edge of space — it would fail eventually — the station had already fulfilled the dreams of its designers.

There had, of course, been opportunities to put one over on their American rivals, especially during the 1980 Moscow Olympics. With the world's press present, cosmonauts read out, live via TV, a prepared statement lauding international socialism and brotherhood. Later, the same crew hurled insults down upon the heads of the defeated Russian basketball team. This, of course, wasn't relayed.

In the middle of the Olympics, the Russians sent a Vietnamese cosmonaut up to Salyut: Pham Tuan, a war hero who, claimed the Soviets, had shot down an American B 52 over Hanoi and whose task aboard the space station was to photograph the effects upon his battered country of US bombs and chemicals. It was a great coup, somewhat lost on the bewildered sports hacks.

There had also been dramas along the road. Another crew made a hasty abort from orbit, pulling 10gs on the way down, but they landed in one piece. Said the commander, with considerable sangfroid: 'Machinery is only machinery; things can go wrong.'

On the eve of his 40th birthday, marathon man Valeri Ryumin made an unscheduled spacewalk to free a jammed radio telescope, which he achieved by one hefty application of a space boot.

Most cosmonauts suffered from spacesickness, some had to be carried from their landing capsule, and all hated the fearsome exercise routines, during which they were obliged to 'walk' and 'jog' for six miles each day. There were no exceptions — the routines were enforced mercilessly.

After Kovalyonok and Savinykh had cleared a space for their kit, it was time for the routine maintenance tasks: repairing pumps, changing circuits and fixing the colour TV set. The chores over, the two cosmic janitors relaxed in front of the TV and viewed selections from their video library.

A week later they had visitors, one of whom was a 'guest' from Mongolia, whose proud father told Soviet newsmen: 'When my son was small he took part in horse races. Now he has saddled a spaceship!'

The four men toiled away, growing orchids — one of the few plants to survive zero-g, manufacturing semiconductor crystals — and testing out a holographic TV link that would allow scientists on the ground to monitor experiments in 3-D.

A the end of March, the Photons (Kovalyonok retained his old callsign) said farewell to their visitors and went back to business.

Six out of every ten working hours were devoted to studying earth, its seas and atmosphere. Of particular interest to the Photons was the Caribbean and its associated weather patterns. At certain times, the Caribbean waters became transparent: the cosmonauts could see all the way down to the ocean floor, with its ridges, furrows, sunken reefs and canyons. It was like a new land beneath the waves.

There was another reason for the Photons' interest in the Caribbean. Further north, along the Florida coast, they could see the Cape and the preparations for Columbia's maiden flight.

NASA's space lemon was on the pad, and hundreds of thousands of Americans were there to watch. Not since the launch of Apollo 11 had so many gathered at the Cape.

On the early morning of 12 April, 1981, twenty years to the day since Yuri Gagarin thundered out of Baikonur, America prepared to re-enter the space race. It had been six years since astronauts last rode the fire.

There stood Columbia, bolted to the big fuel tank, itself strapped onto two massive solid boosters, outlined white against the dawn backdrop by a battery of floodlights. The whole stack resembled some strange religious monument, a cathedral built to honour technology.

High above the ground, waiting patiently for lift-off, were John Young and

The birth of a new space era: Columbia hightails it towards the heavens.

Bob Crippen, the first space pilots of the new era.

John Young had come a long way since the dawn of the space age. When Sputnik coasted around the world and struck terror into the hearts of Americans, Young was a 27-year-old test pilot. Now, nearly a quarter of a century later, he'd made four spaceflights and walked on the moon. No matter that he was 50 and wearing glasses. He had outlasted his contemporaries — Neil Armstrong, Jim Lovell and Pete Conrad — who dubbed him 'Mr Reliable'. John Young was the reigning NASA pilot supreme, and here he was, sitting on top of five million gallons of LOX and liquid hydrogen; inside a spacecraft which had never been flown, powered by engines which had never been flight-tested; strapped to the side of two giant solid boosters never before used on a manned flight; with no escape system except ejector seats.

For Bob Crippen it was even worse. He was on his first flight.

They lay on their backs in the darkness, waiting for dawn to break, not knowing whether the launch would go or be scrubbed.

'Both Crip and I were fairly nervous,' Young admitted later. 'Anybody who's not apprehensive about climbing on top of the first-time flight of a liquid hydrogen-oxygen rocket ship really doesn't understand the problem.'

Dawn rose, and the countdown continued. Just after 7.00 am, Cape time, with 27 seconds to go, Bob Crippen finally accepted it was for real. His heartbeat shot up to 130. Young's stayed below 90. Mr Reliable had been there before.

When the count reached zero, Young and Crippen heard a muffled roar from the three main engines behind Columbia's tail. While they built up to full power, ground or the crew still had the option to scrub. Once the boosters were lit, however, Columbia had to go. Solid rockets could not be switched off.

The entire 2,000-ton stack swayed as the main engines reached full throttle. Then the solids thundered into life, the hold-down bolts blew, Columbia cleared the launch tower and headed towards space, riding a 600-ft tail of fire.

Just two minutes into the flight, the two pilots saw a bright flash as thrusters pushed the spent solids away towards the Atlantic. They were 30 miles up, riding upside-down beneath the big fuel tank. That too was cast off, the main engines cut out. Columbia was on its own, coasting silently towards orbit.

'What a view! What a view!' exclaimed Crippen, looking at the earth from space for the first time.

'It hasn't changed any,' replied Young laconically.

To get them into orbit, Young fired up Columbia's manoeuvring engines, one either side of the tail.

They had made it. John Young and Bob Crippen were in orbit. Columbia had proved a true gem. Now Crippen had to open the cargo bay doors, which acted as radiators, bleeding heat from Columbia's electronics off into space. As the big doors inched open, Crippen peered through the rear window towards the earth above him. Young was staring out the wrap-around front windshield. Both men were amazed: it was like seeing the planet in Cinemascope. Even Young had never seen such a sight. Then Crippen noticed dark patches on the engine pods.

'Hey, John,' he called, 'we've got some tiles missing.'

Back at Mission Control, it was Paranoia Gulch. Missing tiles! A fiery death during re-entry!

The astronauts weren't too concerned. It looked as though the tiles, which were non-critical, had flexed off the highly-curved pods during launch. Those beneath the wings and belly curved gently.

Mission Control only breathed easy after Young rolled Columbia over and exposed its underbelly to the Air Force's big cameras, which were so powerful they could spot a missing tile from the ground.

Columbia's crew spent their first day in space checking the spaceplane.

Between chores, they watched the breathtaking panorama of the Himalayas, thunderheads over the Amazon, and the Bahamas, which Young thought looked like glowing emeralds. They slept in their seats the first night, just in case.

Columbia was working perfectly. After two days, two nights and 36 sunrises, Young and Crippen programmed the computers for re-entry and closed the bay doors. Without the doors closed they couldn't re-enter — Crippen would have had to spacewalk and crank them shut by hand.

They faced the last great unknown: re-entry. Would the tiles handle the heat? Could they control Columbia's 100-ton bulk? Would they break up, high in the stratosphere?

Columbia was flying tail-first and upside down. Young fired up the manoeuvring engines and, as the big spaceplane lost speed, flipped it over, raising the nose so that belly and wings would bear the brunt of re-entry.

They passed over Guam at around 15,000 mph and entered the radio blackout zone. Young and Crippen were on their own. Back at Mission Control, fingers were crossed. Columbia would either come through in one piece or not at all.

Out of the corners of their eyes, the pilots noticed orange blips outside the ship. These were the thruster firings, keeping Columbia steady. They couldn't see them in the vacuum of space. Columbia had hit air. Slowly, a ruddy glow enveloped Columbia's nose. They were inside the re-entry furnace. Young thought it was like flying through a neon tube, smoothly. There was none of the turbulence they'd been told to expect.

John Young, the first American to ride the fire five times, greases Columbia onto the runway.

For the first time ever, pilots were flying a controlled pinpoint re-entry. Young and Crippen were aiming for Edwards Air Force Base, California, out of which X-15 rocket planes had probed the stratosphere two decades before Columbia — but they could have selected any long runway inside 2,000 miles. San Francisco and Los Angeles were within easy reach.

Young threw Columbia into a series of 'S' curves, losing speed and height. Every time he moved his joystick, the flight computers responded with perfectly-judged thruster firings, keeping Columbia right on the line. NASA's space lemon was flying like a dream.

As the air grew denser, Columbia metamorphosed from spaceship to winged glider and the computers shifted their commands from thrusters to wing flaps and rudder. By the time Young and Crippen sighted the coast of California, Columbia's airspeed was down to 5,000mph.

Young took over manual control, flew Columbia in a turn along central California — trailing a double sonic boom — lost more height and speed over the Mojave Desert, circled the runway at Edwards, approached at 250mph, then greased the 100-ton glider on to the tarmac like he was landing on eggs.

And so, as America entered the third decade of man in space to the sound of squealing brakes, John Young — the only pilot to fly Gemini, Apollo and Shuttle, the first American to ride the fire five times — assumed, in perpetuity, the title of 'compleat astronaut'.

Instead of being rescued from a wallowing capsule like drowning rats, John Young and Bob Crippen left Columbia by the front door and walked down to the tarmac. Real spacemen emerging from a real spaceship! The first truckers of outer space! This was true Buck Rogers style!.

And how the crowds loved it! There were a quarter of a million of them out in the scrubby desert surrounding Edwards, and they had all turned out to welcome Columbia home. Many of them sported T-shirts, bearing the legend, in block letters: EAT YOUR HEARTS OUT, RUSSIANS.

Across the country, workers downed tools, teachers interrupted their classes, and millions headed towards the nearest TV sets. Not since Apollo 11 had Americans demonstrated such pride over a space flight.

'Through you,' President Ronald Reagan told the astronauts, 'we feel like giants again.'

The media went to town. One newspaper cartoon showed a grinning Uncle Sam emerging from Columbia, arms raised high like those of a victorious boxer. The *Chicago Tribune* went further:

'It appears we will get into a space arms race whether we like it or not. So fly aloft, Columbia! Deliver your laser guns and satellite busters and spy eyes. Build your battlestars. May the Force be with you!'

Even the London *Times* jumped on the bandwagon:

'The conquest of space is both a necessary expression of man's drive to explore and understand his environment and a military requirement if the West is not to be dominated by Soviet activity in space.'

Time magazine offered an explanation for the fervour:

'The Shuttle had become a kind of technological Rocky, the bum who perseveres to the end, the underdog who finally wins.'

This was true, but it didn't explain such a display of anti-Soviet sentiment, to which the Russians replied in similar style:

'People in the Pentagon are gleefully rubbing their hands. After all, more than two-thirds of the Shuttle flights are to be made in the Pentagon's interests. . . The Pentagon regards the Shuttle as a spacecraft intended for shooting down the enemy's satellites or seizing and bringing them to the vehicle in the role of an omnipotent and insatiable space pirate.'

Eat your hearts out, Russians! Build your battlestars! Insatiable space pirates! This wasn't the admiration expressed by Russia after the success of Apollo 11, or America's condolences in the wake of the Soyuz 11 deaths, nor the

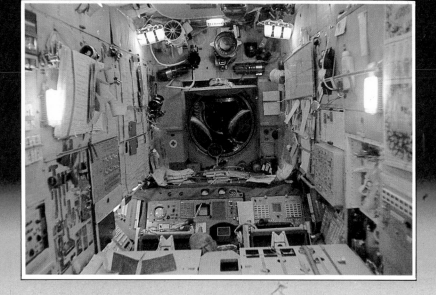

mutual PR of Apollo-Soyuz. This was the rhetoric of the fifties, the crowing and accusations and hurling of insults, and it reflected the increasing political and military confrontation between Russia and America in the eighties: the new Cold War, in which space would play a vital role.

Only Senator Willian Proxmire, NASA's critic, appeared to be immune to overreaction. 'I've never seen so much hype in my life. We're launching a truck into space, and everyone keeps saying it's the Second Coming,' he declared. While Young and Crippen made their brief jaunt into space on the world's first reuseable space truck, the Photons were busy aboard Salyut. A Soviet research ship — which was probably monitoring Columbia's launch — had discovered a giant whirlpool in the Bermuda Triangle, that mysterious area around which myths grew like seaweed. One of the Photon's tasks was to photograph that whirlpool.

Like their Skylab counterparts, Salyut crews regarded earth observation as a pastime rather than work. They would spend hours staring out of the portholes at the changing seasons, cloudscapes — night-time tropical storms were a favourite — and the world ocean with its ever-changing patterns. Some cosmonauts became so adept at 'space vision' that they could identify all the highways around Moscow, even naming familiar streets.

Earth photography and mapping had become the top priority work aboard Salyut, saving, said the Russians, billions of roubles. Again, cosmonauts were exploiting the peculiar properties of earth orbit — in this case altitude — to make space pay.

Kovalyonok and Savinykh received their last visitors in the middle of May. The new arrivals rode the last Soyuz into orbit. From now on, cosmonauts would fly the new Soyuz-T model which was stacked full of the latest

Sunset from Salyut. While America wrestled with Shuttle, Soviet cosmonauts were busy turning earth orbit into a new economic frontier.

(inset) The end of Salyut 6: a cluttered, empty hulk. Since 1977, the station has been home to five cosmonaut expeditions and eleven visitor flights.

technology and had room for three crewmen and their spacesuits. On board Soyuz 40 was the last 'guest' cosmonaut, a Romanian who — since his government refused to toe the Moscow line — had been hanging around the cosmonaut centre for years until the Russians relented and gave him a seat on the final Salyut 6 flight.

Not all the Soviet space scientists approved of guests: 'Soyuz is not a trolleybus,' one grumbled. If they wanted to fly, the 'guests' must work their passage.

So the two crews beavered away, producing silicon crystals in plate form to determine whether silicon-based solar cells could be manufactured in orbit. This was another step along the road towards truly self-sufficient space stations. Salyut already recycled water and crews had experimented with dozens of plants and vegetables grown in hydroponic gardens in the hope that one day cosmonauts might be supplied with oxygen as well as fresh vegetables.

By the time their visitors left, Kovalyonok knew that Salyut 6 had grown too old. It was time to abandon ship.

On the 26 May 1981, twenty years and six weeks since a cosmonaut first rode the fire into earth orbit, Kovalyonok and Savinykh paid their respects to Salyut 6 and floated into Soyuz T-4.

As they backed slowly away, the Photons looked at their home in space for the last time: a stubby telescope-shape with three solar wings, discoloured by the sun and pitted by tiny meteoroids.

'It was so beautiful it gave my heart a pang,' said Kovalyonok.

The Photons landed in good health. Russian newspapers greeted their return with banner headlines lauding their 'New Victory In Space', then announced that there would be no more cosmonaut flights for the rest of the year.

The last men to live and work aboard Salyut 6 were given the traditional Kremlin welcome, at which Leonid Brezhnev outlined Russia's space future:

'Now we have to embark on the next step — to put into orbit permanent research complexes with changing shifts of crews . . . Cosmonauts will be kept busy. There is fascinating and vital work to be done.'

High above him rolled the empty hulk of Salyut 6: home, since 1977, to five cosmonaut expeditions and eleven visitor flights, all of whom had returned safely.

Russian spacemen now rode into orbit aboard sophisticated Soyuz-T ferries. Their home in space was supplied with food, air, water, fuel and spare parts by cheap, automated Progress cargo tenders. Both spacecraft were launched by a modernised version of Sergei Korolev's original semyorka.

Cosmonauts had learned how to adjust to the physical and mental rigours of life above the clouds. They had exploited the strange environment of earth orbit for commercial gain and scientific knowledge.

Russians on the ground had mastered the techniques of spaceship design, the intricacies of automatic docking, and the routine of regular flights to the edge of space.

'All this activity,' commented **Newsweek**, 'has revived the old question of just who is winning the space race.'

Since the launch of Salyut 6, Americans had spent just two days in space. Their rivals had amassed two years' flight time. The USA had slipped into second place in the competition to colonise earth orbit.

NASA had taken a giant gamble with Shuttle, and now the agency was in deep trouble. Shuttle had creamed off so much money from other agency projects that America had effectively killed off its ambitious plans for the exploration of the solar system. One by one, the successors to Mariner, Viking and Voyager were pared down or dropped altogether. NASA had run out of cash.

'The most endangered species at the moment is the exploration of space,' claimed **New Scientist** magazine.

New model Soyuz-T leaves the Baikonur pad. The next step, say the Soviets, is a permanent base on the edge of space.

Inside Salyut mission control. Soviet space engineers are already preparing for 'Kosmograd'—a city on the edge of space.

And so NASA entered the third decade of man in space with Shuttle and little else. Despite the success of Columbia, America's 'space truck' had just one role: as a launcher of satellites. The old dreams of space stations, moonbases and expeditions to the planets were long gone. Astronauts would be truck drivers, not explorers.

With NASA reeling, America's only growth area in space belonged to the generals, who were pumping $8 billion a year into the new high ground where, in the ominous words of one officer, 'the next war may be won'.

'We are now poised to really capitalise on the advantages that space offers us in the defense of our national interest,' gruffed another general, echoing his predecessors of the 60s.

These 'advantages' were to be exploited by a new branch of the armed forces, the US Space Command, which would operate a vast new Shuttle launch site on the coast of California. It was estimated that around half of all Shuttle cargoes would belong to the Pentagon.

In addition to the fleet of military satellites which already patrolled the new high ground, Space Command was planning the biggest space venture since Project Apollo.

Responding to evidence that the Soviet Union was stepping up its own military space programme, President Ronald Reagan delivered what was popularly dubbed his 'Star Wars' speech, urging America to arm itself against the new Soviet threat from the heavens.

It was like the paranoid 60s writ anew in the technical jargon of the 1980s: ASATs, particle beam and laser weapons, space-based sensors, high-speed battle management computers. Shuttles acting as orbiting command posts.

Night-time liftoff for the second Shuttle, Challenger. For the first time in its history, NASA is forced to share a space project with the military, who plan to use Shuttle to take the new Cold War into space.

and even Space Command battle stations high above the clouds.

The scenario was straight out of sci-fi: robot spacecraft armed with missiles, lasers or beam-weapons would intercept Soviet ICBMs while laser-armed Shuttles zapped Russian spysats and Salyuts; the latter armed to the teeth with lasers and missiles and defended by Soviet Shuttles.

Battle stations on the edge of space! Duelling Shuttles! Lasers zapping enemy missiles! Beam weapons! Space Marines!

It would cost billions of dollars, and it was a new and deadly acceleration of the arms race above the clouds: a heavenly arms race which had already consumed over a hundred billion dollars since the launch of Sputnik.

Back in the real world, NASA was proving that Shuttle, despite its extravagance, would transform earth orbit. The agency's engineers were busy churning out plans for stations, factories and power stations on the edge of space, while Columbia and its sister ship, Challenger, racked up success after success.

Twenty years after Valentina Tereshkova rode the fire from Baikonur, Dr Sally K. Ride became America's first spacewoman. The flight, which one newspaper termed 'the most ballyhooed space shot since Neil Armstrong stepped on the moon' was accompanied by a press barrage not seen since the 1960s:

'Super Sally' . . . 'Space Shuttle Wonder Woman' . . . 'Sal Takes Lipstick For Smart Landing,' they drooled, not forgetting to mention that she was 'a shapely brunette' whose flight had 'rekindled the American love affair with space flight'.

Down at the Cape, tourists sported T-shirts urging her to 'Ride, Sally, Ride', while the competent physicist and flight engineer helped launch two comsats from the Shuttle's cargo hold and proclaimed: 'It is time people realised that women can do any job they want to.'

The flight of Sally Ride was a boon for NASA's new PR effort — as was that of Guion Bluford, America's first black astronaut — but the agency was still in deep trouble. As well as the lack of finance, the cutbacks of planetary spacecraft and the limited future of Shuttle as a 'space truck', NASA was under fire from Congressional critics for its involvement with the military, who had added muscle to Shuttle's financing and were now looking for the payoff. The 'civilian' agency was launching military payloads. NASA could no longer claim to be the peaceful arm of the American space effort.

There was even talk of splitting up the agency altogether.

By the 1980s, space had become big business, the new industrial frontier. Revenue from comsats alone was worth several billions of dollars a year.

Other nations and even private enterprise was competing with the agency for the profitable business of launching satellites. The Europeans had their own rocket, Arlane, and were busy wooing commercial clients. Inside the US,

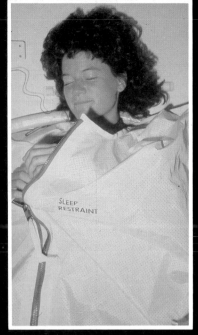

'Space Shuttle Wonder Woman'—Sally Ride, first American woman to ride the fire, naps in zero-g sleeping bag. Meanwhile, NASA is in deep trouble.

private consortia were planning to lease rockets or Shuttle flights from NASA, or build their own launchers. Even the Russians were touting around the market, offering to loft satellites atop their big Proton rocket. NASA no longer possessed a monopoly.

It was suggested that NASA should hive off Shuttle to private enterprise and concentrate on the unmanned exploration of the Solar System, or hand over the selling of Shuttle flights to brokers. Even the NASA boss, James Beggs, suported such a move.

For the first time in a quarter of a century, it looked as if the Big Machine would be broken up.

To survive, the agency desperately needed a Project Apollo, a scheme for man-in-space so grandiose that it would restore NASA to its old pre-eminence; a bold step towards the new world above the clouds.

There was really only one candidate. The moon and planets were out, at least for the foreseeable future. The robots had proved their worth too well.

The obvious choice was a permanent space station — an orbiting laboratory, factory and repair shop into which Shuttle would fit as it had been intended a decade before, when the engineers dreamed of Shuttles ferrying men and material to a base high above the clouds, where men and women would toil, as colonists, and perhaps venture out to the moon and planets.

No-one doubted that such a station was possible — Skylab and the Salyuts had paved the way — but whether NASA would ever raise the money for such an expensive venture seemed doubtful.

By contrast, Russia was pouring roubles into space. For every spacecraft launched by America, the Soviet Union launched three. In April 1982, Salyut 7 roared heavenwards; a new home on the edge of space. Sputnik's 25th anniversary was celebrated by new record-breaking cosmonaut feats and more test-flights of the small Russian Shuttle.

In March of '83, the Soviet Union took a new step towards the colonisation of space. Engineers lofted a 12-ton space station into orbit and docked it with Salyut 7, almost doubling the station's size. The section, 'Star', came complete with supplies, engines and solar panels. Stars could be used as freighters, tugs or science labs — or even as the building blocks from which, like Lego, a new generation of Soviet space stations could be assembled on the edge of space. The 'permanent research complex' was becoming a reality.

It already had a name — 'Kosmograd' or 'Space City' — and it would be the first true permanent space colony: bearing the Red Flag, not the Stars and Stripes. Soviet engineers were already planning regular three-month 'tours of duty' aboard Salyut 7 to prepare cosmonauts for their new life in space.

The new year of 1984 brought with it the US Presidential elections, and the first signs that NASA might avoid the surgeon's knife. Spacelab, the joint US-European laboratory which rode inside Shuttle's cargo bay and which had

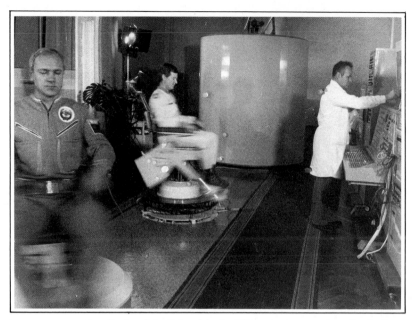

(right) Frenchman Jean Chretien (background) joins his Russian commander on the revolving chair—one Soviet 'cure' for the debilitating effects of weightlessness. Soon, the two men will fly to the new station, Salyut 7.

(left) The second woman into space—and, again, she's a Russian. Svetlana Savitskaya on her homecoming from Salyut 7.

(far right inset) Challenger above, earth below. America, though behind the Russians in the race to colonise earth orbit, takes giant steps to catch up—and Shuttle is just the beginning.

(far right) Trailing fire and smoke, Challenger races above the clouds. President Reagan gives the go-ahead for America's own 'Kosmograd'—and the new assault on space has begun.

been proposed as the basic building block of the US space station, finally flew — years behind schedule and millions of dollars over budget. Spacelab was pronounced a success, and the engineers breathed again. More grist to NASA's mill came in the form of a Congressional report which confirmed what the engineers had known all along — that the Soviet Union had overtaken America in the race to establish a permanent colony in earth orbit.

The news from Washington was encouraging: NASA's lobbying for a space station was reaching receptive ears within the Reagan Administration. John Glenn, the first American to orbit the earth, was hitting the campaign trail for the Democratic nomination. Glenn, now 62, appealed to the same constituency as Reagan — white middle Americans — and was regarded as a threat to the president's re-election plans. 'This is a way to knock his socks off', gloated a White House aide, referring to Reagan's expected approval of NASA's proposals.

The signs were auspicious. An election coming up, evidence that the Russians were restoring their old space pre-eminence, and Reagan did just as Johnson, Nixon and Kennedy had done before him.

On the 25 January 1984, as part of a State of the Union speech which also offered an olive branch to the Soviet Union, President Ronald Reagan authorised NASA to take the next giant leap towards the heavens. Echoing Kennedy's 1961 inaugural address, Reagan proclaimed that:

'America has always been greatest when we dared to be great. We can reach for greatness again. We can follow our dreams to distant stars, living and working in space for peaceful, economic and scientific gains.'

The engineers were jubilant. NASA had been saved by the election year bell. Billions of dollars would be pumped into the new space station programme, a base on the edge of space which would house rotating crews of up to ten astronauts, to be operating by 1992 — the 500th anniversary of Columbus' discovery of America.

Meanwhile, at the Baikonur Cosmodrome in faraway Kazakhstan, Soviet engineers readied a G-1 'superbooster' for launch. Atop the great rocket, whose earlier catastrophic failures had killed Russian hopes of a moon landing, was the core of the first 12-man Cosmograd space station.

The new assault on space had begun.

Abernathy, Ralph 93
Agena 53, 61-5
Aldrin, Edwin 'Buzz' 61-5, 89-99
Anders, William 78-83
Apollo Project 29, 41-2; Apollo 7 74-7, 127; Apollo 8 73, 77-83, 85, 87, 100, 105; Apollo 9 86-7; Apollo 10 87-9; Apollo 11 89-99, 102, 109, 147, 151; Apollo 12 102-3, 119, 123; Apollo 13 104-9, 110; Apollo 14 104, 110-11; Apollo 15 113, 115; Apollo 16 114; Apollo 17 115-16; Apollo 204 66-8, 108, 144; Apollo-Soyuz 129-33, 152
Arlane 156
Armstrong, Neil 59, 89-99, 102, 115, 116, 144, 149, 156
Artyukhin, Yuri 127-8
Atlas 49

Bassett, Charlie 59, 61
Bean, Al 102-3, 123-4
Beeding, Eli L. 18-19
Beggs, James 157
Belka 22
Belyayev, Pavel 47-8, 72, 78, 83
Beregovoi, Georgi 77
Bluford, Guion 156
Borman, Frank 53-8, 78-83
Brand, Vance 129-33
Brezhnev, Leonid 44-5, 47, 58, 85, 142, 154
Brown, Harold 145
Bykovsky, Valery 45

Carpenter, M. Scott 19, 20, 36-7, 59
Carr, Gerry 80, 124-7, 138
Cernan, Gene 61, 87-9, 115-16
Chaffee, Roger 66-8
Challenger 156
Collins, Michael 61, 89-99
Columbia 143-5, 147-51, 155, 156
Conrad, Pete 52, 61, 102-3, 118-23, 149
Cooper, Leroy Gordon 20, 42-3, 52, 59, 104
Cosmograd 158
Crippen, Bob 149-51
Cronkite, Walter 13, 36
Cunningham, Walt 68, 74-7, 127

Dobrovolsky, Georgi 112-13
DynaSoar 114

Echo 1 22
Eisele, Donn 68, 74-7
Eisenhower, Dwight, D. 14, 17-18, 29-30
Enterprise 143-4
Evans, Ron 115-16
Explorer 1 16

Faith 7 42-3
Farrell, Donald F. 19
Feoktistov, Konstantin 47
Ford, Gerald 129, 132
Freeman, Ted 59
Friendship 7 33-5
Fulton, James 17

G-1 89, 100, 137
Gagarin, Yuri 23-7, 29, 31, 52, 70, 72, 78, 83, 95, 111, 113, 142, 143
Garriott, Owen 123-4
Gemini Project 42, 46, 69; Gemini 1 50; Gemini 2 50; Gemini 3 49-50; Gemini 4 50-2; Gemini 5 52, 119; Gemini 6 53-8; Gemini 7 53-8, 105; Gemini 8 59-61; Gemini 9 59, 61; Gemini 10 61; Gemini 11 61, 119; Gemini 12 61-5
Gibson, Ed 124-7, 138
Glenn, John H. 20, 32-5, 68, 83, 116, 143, 158
Glennan, T. Keith 21, 27
Gordon, Dick 61, 102-3
Grechko, Georgi 128, 135-9
Grissom, Virgil 'Gus' 19, 20, 30-1, 32, 49-50, 59, 66-8, 74
Gubarev, Alexei 128

Haise, Fred 104-9
Ham 17
Haney, Paul 59
Hart, Jane 45
Hitler, Adolf 9, 90
Humphrey, Hubert 68

Ivanchenkov, Alexander 139-42

Johnson, Lyndon B. 13, 19, 52, 65, 68, 92, 158

Kapitsa, Pyotr 100
Kennedy, John F. 22, 27, 29, 30, 41, 69, 74, 89, 92, 115, 158
Kerwin, Joe 119-23
Khrunov, Evgeny 84-5
Khrushchev, Nikita 10-13, 21, 23, 31, 32, 38-9, 43-4, 46, 47, 58, 78
King, Martin Luther 91
Klimuk, Pyotr 61, 89-99
Komarov, Vladimir 47, 69-70, 72, 74, 95, 113
Korolev, Sergei 9-13, 14, 23, 24, 39, 41, 45, 46, 58, 70, 73, 78, 113, 154
Kosygin, Alexei 114
Kovalyonok, Vladimir 139-42, 146-7, 153-4
Kraft, Christopher Columbus 90
Kubasov, Valeri 129-33

Laika 15-16
Lapp, Ralph 78
Lazarev, Vasily 128-9
Leonov, Alexei 47-8, 78, 83, 85, 112, 129-33
Lipmann, Walter 68
Lousma, Jack 123-4
Lovell, Bernard 39
Lovell, Jim 53-8, 61-5, 78-83, 104, 149
Luce, Clare Boothe 45
Luna 9 59
Luna 15 89, 109
Luna 16 109-10
Lunakhod 1 110

Mailer, Norman 110
Makarov, Oleg 128-9, 137
Mao Tse-Tung 43-4
Mariner 2 39-41
Mariner 4 52
Mariner 5 71
Mattingly, Ken 104
Mercury Project 18-27; Mercury 1 27-30; Mercury 2 30-1; Mercury 3 32-5; Mercury 4 36-7; Mercury 5 41; Mercury 6 42-3
MISS Project 18

McDivitt, Jim 50-2, 86-7
McNamara, Robert 30

Nedelin, Marshal 23
Nikolaev, Andrian 38-9, 46, 109
Nixon, Richard M. 22, 74, 85, 92, 95, 97, 99, 102, 108, 109, 111, 113, 114, 129, 158

Orbiter Project 14-16

Paine, Thomas O. 74, 85-6
Patsayev, Viktor 112-13
Pauling, Linus 83
Pioneer V 22
Podgorny, Nikolai 95
Pogue, Bill 124-7, 138
Popovich, Pavel 38-9, 127-8
Progress 1 138
Proton 59, 72, 73
Proxmire, William 129, 152

R-7 12-13, 58, 71, 131
Reagan, Ronald 95, 151, 155, 158
Redstone 23, 27, 49
Remek, Vladimir 138
Ride, Sally K. 156
Romanenko, Yuri 135-9
Ryumin, Valeri 146-7

Salyut 1 111, 112, 113, 122
Salyut 2 118
Salyut 3 127-8
Salyut 4 128, 133, 135, 139
Salyut 5 135
Salyut 6 135-42, 146-7, 152-4
Salyut 7 157
Saturn 39, 59, 65, 74, 79
Savinykh, Viktor 146-7, 153-4
Schirra, Walter H. 20, 41, 53-8, 59, 66, 68, 74-7, 125
Schmitt, Jack 115-16
Schweickart, Rusty 86-7
Scott, Dave 59, 86-7, 113
See, Eliot 59, 61
Sevastyanov, Vitali 109, 133
Shatalov, Vladimir 84-5
Shephard, Alan B. 20, 27-30, 32, 38, 59, 74, 104, 110
Sholokov, Mikhail 46
Skylab 111, 113, 114, 115, 118-27, 135, 136, 152, 157
Slayton, Donald 'Deke' 20, 59, 129-33

Soyuz Project 46; Apollo-Soyuz 129-33, 152; Soyuz 1 69-70; Soyuz 3 77; Soyuz 4 84-5; Soyuz 5 84-5; Soyuz 6 101; Soyuz 10 111; Soyuz 11 112-13, 121, 127, 135, 151; Soyuz 12 127; Soyuz 13 127; Soyuz 14 127; Soyuz 18 128-9; Soyuz 40 152-3; Soyuz T-4 152-3
Spacelab 157-8
Space Shuttle 113, 114, 115, 143-5, 147-51, 154-6
Sputnik 1 13-15
Sputnik 2 15-16
Stafford, Tom 53-8, 61, 87-9, 129-33
Stalin, Joseph 9, 10
Strelka 22
Surveyor 71, 102
Swigert, Jack 104-9

Tereshkova, Valentina 'Valya' 44-6, 85, 142
Titan 49
Titov, Gherman 31-2, 38
Tuan, Pham 147
Tupolev, Anton 9

Vanguard 1 16, 18
V-2 8-9, 10, 13-14, 90, 112
Volynov, Boris 84-5
von Braun, Wernher 8-9, 10, 14, 15, 16, 18, 39, 41, 59, 74, 90, 95, 102, 114, 115
Viking 1 113-5
Viking 2 133-4
Volkov, Vladislav 112-13
Voskhod 1 46-7, 72
Voskhod 2 47-8, 78
Vostock 1 23-7
Vostock 5 45
Vostock 6 45-6
Voyager 144

Wagner, Robert F. 29
Walker, Joe 22
Webb, James 71, 73, 85
Weitz, Paul 119-23
White, Bob 22
White, Ed 50-2
White, Thomas D. 18

X-15 18, 22, 37-8, 59, 90, 114, 151

Yegorov, Boris 47
Yeliseyev, Alexei 84
Yevtushenko, Yevgeny 113
Young, John 49-50, 61, 87-9, 114, 147-51

Zond 4 71-2
Zond 5 73
Zond 6 77-8